RYA Boat Maintenanc

by

© Andrew Simpson, First Published 2013
The Royal Yachting Association
RYA House, Ensign Way, Hamble
Southampton SO31 4YA
Tel: 0844 556 9555 **Fax:** 0844 556 9516
E-mail: publications@rya.org.uk
Web: www.rya.org.uk
Follow us on Twitter:
@RYAPublications #Maintenance
ISBN: 978-1,906435684
RYA Order Code: G104

Totally Chlorine   Sustainable
Free   Forests

All rights reserved. No part of this publication may be reproduced, stored in a retrieval system, or transmitted, in any form or by any means, electronic, mechanical, photocopying, recording or otherwise, without the prior permission in writing of the publishers.

A CIP record of this book is available from the British Library.

Note: While all reasonable care has been taken in the preparation of this book, the publisher takes no responsibility for the use of the methods or products or contracts described in the book.

Cover Design: Pete Galvin
Illustrations: Andrew Simpson
Typeset: KJS Design
Proofreading and indexing: Alan Thatcher
Printed in China through World Print

CONTENTS

INTRODUCTION

Becoming the owner of a boat is a bit like the first days of parenthood. There's a high degree of excitement but – as no doubt many of us remember – along with the joy comes a fair dose of anxiety. Of course, the dazed parents will have made themselves familiar with the basics and are acutely aware that there are vital responsibilities involved. The demanding newcomer will need sustenance, care and cosseting, but exactly what and when and how much is only vaguely understood, distilled incompletely from books and magazine articles or from the dubious reminiscences of others. Detailed skills are lacking. Might you do too much or too little, too often or too seldom? Beneath the jubilation and pride in your new parental status you find yourself musing fearfully on what damage you might inflict by your well-intentioned but bumbling ministrations. Any outward displays of confidence are pure sham. Internally you quake.

For first-timers the prospects can be extremely daunting but you reason that it should get better with experience. Yes? Well, partially but alas never entirely, for the path can take different twists. In my own case I had expected the appearance of a second child, a daughter, to herald a simple rerun of the previous undertaking but this was not to be. Infuriating, perverse – call it what you will – she proved to be a creature of an entirely different cast to her preceding brother and we found ourselves improvising every bit as madly as we had before.

And so it is with boats which, in my experience and surprisingly since they can look identical, are extraordinarily individualistic and given to their own quirks, foibles and characters. No two are exactly the same, meaning that the tasks that sorted out one might not work on another. They will all present their own demands and problems. Fortunately, they also yield rewards.

So this book is a sort of survivors' guide to modern boat maintenance, with the word 'modern' needing qualification. Although many of the topics are common to all boats, I don't intend to cover in any depth ancient or unusual construction techniques which rightly deserve dedicated books of their own. The fact is that we live at a time when moulded reinforced plastic boats comprise the vast majority and it's on these that we shall focus.

Welcome aboard.

CHAPTER 1

How it all began

Those who started boating in the early 1960s and before will probably have started their careers on timber vessels – perhaps planked in the traditional manner by craftsmen of rare and costly skill or built from sheet plywood on a semi-production basis. We have a lot to thank that latter method for, since it plucked boating from the snooty realms of 'yachting' and made 'sailing' much more accessible to the common man. Unhappily, cheap and cheerful these utility boats might have been but durable they were not. Cheaply made, often using inferior glues, their owners waged a ceaseless war against rot and delamination, the long-term futility of their efforts now evidenced by the pitifully few examples that survive to this day.

Fortunately, technology came to the rescue. The end of the 1950s saw the emergence of GRP (Glass Reinforced Plastic) with boatbuilding being its first widespread civilian application. By the mid-1960s the new wonder material had really taken hold and, despite scornful scoffs from the traditionalists, it was greeted with the enthusiasm it deserved. The age of the everlasting boat had arrived!

Well, not quite. We have since learned that GRP comes with its own clutch of problems but boats moulded from it haven't done at all badly, with the vast majority of those ever built still surviving.

Some designs made the transition by degrees. The shapely Kim Holman design *Twister*, for example, started life with

▲ Classic boats gather in Mallorca. Lovely to look at but involving lots of maintenance.

▲ *Nohoh* – although there is some debate, she is believed to be the first GRP yacht built in the UK. Her deck and superstructure are timber.

conventional carvel planking, then appeared with a GRP hull and timber decks before emerging in its final reincarnation as an all-GRP version.

So the *Twister* was an adaptation of a traditional design – and a worthy one at that – but most designers were quick to realise that moulded GRP could be formed into shapes that would have been difficult or commercially impracticable to fashion out of timber. The opportunities were irresistible. There was no going back.

The first GRP boats might have had moulded hull and deck shells but their interiors were fairly conventional, with bulkheads and other accommodation furniture being made out of plywood secured to the shell's interior surfaces with resin and glass 'tabbing'. However, it quickly occurred to those in the business that prefabricated GRP mouldings could also be used in modular form to replace the plywood. For instance, galley units, seating,

even the deckhead lining and shower stall could be made up in the moulding shop and simply bonded into place before the hull and deck came together.

Naturally, the savings in time – and therefore costs – were tremendous, but some boatbuilders rather overdid it, coming up with starkly sterile interiors that had all the charms of milking parlours or hospital sluice rooms.

For most boat owners this was carrying modernity too far. Today's boats might look modern on the outside but the marketing men have since learned that what really sells is to have a cosy interior aglow with acres of veneered plywood all trimmed with a decorative timber such as teak or cherry. However, you only have to look behind the window dressing to find an intricate moulded sub-structure module on which the various panels are mounted – an ingenious fusion of old and new dictated largely by public taste as much as by practicality.

THE BASIC LAMINATE

This is not the place to delve into the chemical mysteries of that composite material described variously as fibreglass, glassfibre or GRP, but, in order to appreciate both its virtues and susceptibilities, it helps to understand the fundamentals. Incidentally, our American friends know GRP as FRP (Fiber Reinforced Plastic) which increasingly these days can be a more accurate description since reinforcing fibres other than glass can be used – aramids (Kevlar®, Twaron® etc) and carbon amongst them. However, for your average run-of-the-mill boat, glass remains the first choice, combining good structural properties with relatively low cost.

As the term 'glass reinforced plastic' so aptly states – and at the risk of irritating you with the blindingly obvious – the two principal ingredients of a GRP laminate are glass and plastic. Both come in various guises.

Glass fibres: It seems preposterous at first thought that an ostensibly shatterable material such as glass could be used so sinuously but it's actually been around for some time. Both the ancient Phoenicians and Egyptians knew how to produce decorative glass strands and, in 1893, the American actress Georgia Cayvan appeared wearing a dress woven from glass fibres – though it's said that she wasn't impressed with either its weight or stiffness and apparently had some difficulty sitting down. The big advance came about in 1938 when US glass makers Owens-Corning developed machinery that could spin glass threads as fine and flexible as silk. Packed into wads that could be stuffed into roof spaces and hollow walls, it was originally intended for insulation.

By a serendipitous convergence of technologies, polyester resins were also appearing around then and the structural potential of combining the two didn't escape the engineers. Constructional applications of the first GRP laminates occurred in about 1942 and within a few years the fabrication techniques had been adopted by boatbuilders. To this day the boatbuilding industry is one of the foremost consumers of GRP materials.

Glass fibres can be sprayed on (with a device known as a 'chopper gun') but more commonly come in large rolls, either woven in some configuration or other (woven rovings) or bound into a coarse felt of short random strands (Chopped Strand Mat – commonly abbreviated to 'CSM'). The woven rovings bestow more strength whereas the CSM will contain a higher proportion of resin, bringing improved resistance to water absorption. In the overall makeup of a GRP laminate, clearly there's a role for both.

▲ A moulded GRP hull waiting to be released. Note the empty mould in the background.

Plastic: Within our limited remit, the 'plastic' most familiar to us is a thermosetting polymer known as 'polyester'. A thermoset plastic is one which hardens irreversibly – that's to say it can't be returned to its original state by melting. The boatbuilder buys the resin in a liquid form and adds precise quantities of chemicals (catalysts and accelerators) to it which causes the resin to solidify.

Polyester resins come in various forms but the two we're most interested in are:

- **Gelcoat.** A high-grade thixotropic (thickened) resin, usually coloured with pigments to form a decorative finish.

- **Laminating resin.** A lower viscosity resin used in combination with the glass fibres to build up the structural laminate.

THE MOULDING PROCESS

It should come as no surprise to learn that in order to build moulded components you need a mould. These are female representations of the finished part and are also almost invariably constructed of GRP. Since the fairness and quality of finish is dependent on the precision of the mould, it goes without saying that they are made and maintained with great care. Most boatbuilders will tell you that their moulds are their most valuable assets.

A typical moulding sequence – let's say the hull – might go like this:

- The waxed and polished face of the mould is coated with pigmented gelcoat, usually sprayed on but sometimes using paint-type rollers. Two coats are usually applied, allowing the first to harden before applying the next. Remember, the gelcoat is all any outsider will see of the finished hull.

- Once the gelcoat has set, a single resin-rich layer of CSM is laid over the gelcoat, either sprayed on with a chopper gun, or 'hand laid' with buckets of catalysed

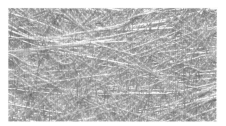

▲ **Chopped Strand Mat (CSM).**

resin and rollers. Either way, a special roller, often comprising a number of metal washers, is used to consolidate the laminate and force air bubbles from it. This is a very important process, particularly with this outermost layer of the hull (sometimes called the 'skin coat'), which will be the next defence against water absorption after the gelcoat.

- Again, this is allowed partially to 'cure' – at least hard enough not to be disturbed by further work. The remainder of the laminate thickness is then built up progressively, usually by alternating layers of CSM with woven rovings, with additional reinforcements in high-load areas such as the keel. This will probably need to be done in several stages over a few days because the chemical changes taking place within the resin generate exothermic heat which could damage the laminate if excessive.

▲ **Woven rovings.**

And that's just about it; job done. The hull will be allowed time to cure further before being released from the mould and trimmed. There's only the other components to mould and the assembling and fitting out to do – in reality at least 95 per cent of the work!

CHAPTER 2

Take care of your topsides

THE CHALLENGES

There's no doubt about it: boating is tough on boats. If we really wanted to look after them we would leave them blocked off ashore, safe from harm. For most of us this is hardly a practical solution, so every spring sees us committing perhaps our most treasured possession into the hostile waters on which we go boating.

But, before we investigate the various external threats in more detail, let's kick off with a short but true tale – a tale which could deserve the title of ....

THREAT NUMBER ONE: THE OVERZEALOUS BOAT OWNER

An acquaintance of mine is a fastidious man. He's owned the same boat since new – a period of nearly twenty years. During the lay-up period ashore he works on it almost every available moment, pottering happily away through his regular maintenance regime, fussing over the smallest detail. We could hardly meet without him quizzing me on some microscopic defect he had discovered. Anxiety was his normal state.

Then, one day, I came upon him unloading a cardboard box from his car. It contained a brand new electric polisher of industrial proportions, far more powerful than the dainty one I had seen him wielding before.

'Pinholes,' he told me glumly. 'I've found pinholes in the gelcoat. And some shadowy dark patches. I'm going to polish them out.'

So it fell to me to suggest that he get his cash back on the polisher while it was still in unused condition, and also to break the bad news. The pinholes and shadowy patches were a sign that the gelcoat was nearing the end of its useful life – at least in the cosmetic sense. What I didn't have the heart to tell him was that his own enthusiasm for polishing had hastened its end. He had virtually polished away the gelcoat to extinction.

In truth, he would have done well to have followed one of the fundamentals of medical ethics: *Primum non nocere* – First Do No Harm.

This should be good news for any boat owners who, one would think, might prefer to take pleasure in their boats rather than toil over them. Compared to traditional wooden vessels, whose upkeep involves an onerous treadmill of care and maintenance, GRP boats are remarkably tolerant of the abuse we throw at them. The wise skipper should take advantage of their forbearance and enjoy them without fretting. In boat maintenance, as in other matters, we should remember that LESS IS OFTEN MORE.

From here on in we'll be looking at those non-personal factors that threaten the condition of our boats, the defensive action we can take to protect them, and then the remedies that might be appropriate when damage of whatever kind occurs.

We should bear in mind that it's not just water, fresh or salty. Tars and oils float on the surface, flotsam and jetsam the same. The sun-warmed upper layers teem with micro-organisms that will attach themselves to your hull to foul or stain. Wave action,

▲ **From the durability standpoint, blue is a poor choice for gelcoat.**

spray and the heeling power in sails or the slamming caused by powerful engines will make sure that this far from impeccable bio-soup reaches every inch of the exterior gelcoat.

If anything, it gets worse when we come into port. Now we're alongside a quay or pontoon, or rafted up with a gaggle of other boats. Airborne grit settles where it can – a fine but relentless abrasive. The odd thump or scrape is commonplace, for everyone gets it wrong occasionally. Granted, we rig fenders to absorb the worst of the punishment, but these only afford partial protection and, anyway, can carry yet more grit and dirt. However careful we are, a season's boating will leave its battle scars, so it's hardly surprising that boats return home looking more bedraggled than when they left.

Let's look at the various natural threats in more detail.

BAD NEWS ABOUT BLUE

Above all other colours, blue is the one most associated with the sea. Unfortunately, it's not the most suitable and to understand why we must talk a little physics.

We're all familiar with the visible light spectrum, as represented by rainbows. At one end of the spectrum lies blue (shorter wavelength) with red (longer wavelength) at the other end. Just outside the visible red lies infrared which we can only experience as *heat*.

No object has intrinsic colour. The sensation we know as colour is reflected light. For an object to look red, the blue end of the spectrum is absorbed and the red end reflected. And for an object to appear blue the reverse is the case – which is the root of our problem. The price of achieving that smart nautical blue is that the red (heat) end of the spectrum must be absorbed. And heat being one of the principal causes of weathering ... well, need I go on?

Compare red and blue surfaces on a sunny day. The blue will be considerably hotter – bad news for the gelcoat.

FADING

The villains responsible for fading are solar radiation, temperature and water – all of which conspire to attack and oxidise the pigmented gelcoat. Over the years the surface takes on a chalky appearance and the colour density can become patchy – more faded in some places than in others.

In the early days of GRP boats, most manufacturers offered a range of hull colours. Not anymore. With a very few exceptions, the only option nowadays is white (or nearly so, there being an astonishing number of shades of this seemingly neutral tone). This apparently high-handed restriction on customer choice isn't motivated by simple cost cutting – though of course standardisation does produce savings – but more as a defence against future grievance. All pigmented gelcoats fade, but colours – particularly dark colours (see panel on page 9) – fade more noticeably. Boring it might look, but at least white gelcoat has the thoughtfulness to fade to... well, a slightly different shade of white, with the variation over time being relatively inconspicuous.

In short the manufacturers have learned not to invite trouble by offering colours where any fading will soon become apparent. Fewer complaints roll in when the damage isn't obvious. An oblivious customer remains a happy one is their philosophy. And who can blame them?

Before we move on, it should be emphasised that having shiny topsides is more than just vanity. The deeper the gloss, the more light will be reflected back – including those UV rays that can do so much damage.

Of course, all good things come to an end. The life of any coating is finite. Let's face it, if you were to leave your car parked out in the street for twenty years you would expect its paintwork to look a bit tatty, wouldn't you? If you were also to hose it down every day with salt water it would be considered outright vandalism. Over time, reversing the process becomes more and more difficult. But that doesn't necessarily mean it can't be done. If an adequate thickness of gelcoat remains, there may still be something you can do to improve the situation.

KEEPING THE GLEAM

All boats need a regular wash down with soapy fresh water to remove the superficial grime that accumulates. Use a soft-bristled boat brush to help dislodge obstinate particles and remember to rinse thoroughly once you're done. Older boats may need more attention.

So, starting with the newest...

■ **General Protection** – a high-quality boat wax, applied at least twice a year – more often if the boat is washed frequently. 3M's Scotchgard Marine Liquid Wax® or Star Brite's Boat Wax® fall into this category. Avoid automobile type products which are often excessively loaded with silicones that could prove troublesome later on.

■ **Lightly oxidised** – By now the gelcoat is losing its lustre and there will be light chalking – probably almost indiscernible on white or near-white hulls. The product to use now is a combined cleaner/wax product that contains a relatively mild abrasive rubbing compound. 3M's Marine Fiberglass Cleaner and Wax® is such a product.

■ **Medium to heavy oxidisation** – This calls for sterner stuff, beyond the scope of a multi-purpose product. Now you need the two-pronged approach of removing the oxidised layer with a buffing (also called 'rubbing' or 'cutting') compound, followed by a wax polish to add the final gleam plus ongoing protection. There are a number of brands on the market: 3M Marine Super Duty Rubbing Compound® and the Farecla range to name but two. Most compound systems come in various grades. In principle, you start with the most aggressive and get finer for the final finish. However, you will find that your local chandler stocks a single grade that will do the whole job in most cases.

It is possible to complete these tasks by hand, but it's much easier to use an electric polisher, working a small area at a time so whatever compound or wax you're working with doesn't get the chance to dry. Recommendations vary between manufacturers but rotation speeds of 1500–2500rpm is the usual advice. Beware of angle grinders, which look similar to polishers but have rotation speeds often exceeding 6000rpm. Foam or white lambswool pads are usually used for cutting compounds and softer lambswool pads for polishing. Foam pads can generate too much surface heat and need to be used carefully.

Important points to remember are:

■ *Always start by making sure the surface is clean and dust free to prevent dirt being driven into the surface.*

■ *Work on smallish areas at a time. 50cm x 50cm is about right. Spread the compound evenly over the area – a paintbrush being a useful tool for this.*

■ *Don't allow the compound to dry or it might burn the gelcoat. This often means you shouldn't work when the surface is heated by the sun – particularly the case with dark gelcoats. Apply it and use it immediately is the rule.*

■ *When machine buffing, only apply moderate pressure. Too much and the resulting friction will overheat the gelcoat.*

▲ **To remove heavy oxidisation it helps to use an electric polisher – but be very, very careful with its use!**

■ *Keep the buffing pad flat or nearly so. Never use the edge of the pad, which can cause burning.*

■ *Use only clean pads. Dried-on dirt or old compound can cause scratches. Most types of pad are washable.*

■ *Don't allow the compound, wax or pads to become contaminated with anything that might scratch the surface. Never place pads face down between sessions.*

■ **AND REMEMBER:** *Do no more than you have to. EVERY process reduces the gelcoat thickness.*

STAINS

You've washed the boat off but some soiling still remains, typically just above the waterline and in the region of the exhaust outlet. The waterline staining is almost certainly caused by algae which took up residence when the boat was afloat. The word 'algae' (the singular is alga) covers a large group of diverse aquatic organisms, ranging from the kelp you'll find on the beach to those tiny unicellular pests that turn swimming-pool

▲ **Revenge of the micro-organisms – waterline staining will make any boat look tatty.**

water green. The colour green is significant. Although, confusingly, not all algae belong to the vegetable kingdom, most are photoautotrophic. This means that they rely on photosynthesis for their food supply and therefore contain chlorophyll. That stain above your waterline started off green but is now brown because the algae are dead.

What to do

It's time to reach for some stain remover. These are usually gels or liquids, but at least one brand comes as a powder. They contain phosphoric or oxalic acid which will bleach away both algal and exhaust stains without damaging the gelcoat. You may hear that the smart thing to do is to lay your hands on some oxalic acid crystals and make up your own cleaning solution, but be careful. Oxalic acid is the stuff that makes rhubarb leaves poisonous. If inhaled or ingested, it can cause ulceration to your airways and gastro-intestinal tract – in serious cases enough to cause death. (Incidentally, should anyone be unlucky or daft enough to take a swig, don't induce vomiting. It will do just as

much damage on the way out as it did on the way in. Try and make the casualty drink lots of water and seek medical assistance immediately.)

Stain removers work better in warmish conditions, so this is a job for the spring. Paint the goop liberally on to the stained area and leave it for 10–15 minutes to do its job. Light staining should disappear in a single hit. For stubborn stains you may have to repeat the operation a few times. Once you're satisfied, rinse off with fresh water, step back and admire.

BATTLE SCARS

No matter how careful we are, the chances of surviving a season without suffering at least some minor damage are small. Even if our own boat-handling skills are faultless we often find ourselves at the mercy of other crews' clumsiness, most notably in marinas.

Of course, serious incidents almost invariably trigger insurance claims, but few of us would negate our no-claims bonuses for trivial scrapes and dinks, so it often falls on us to repair – or have repaired – the more minor damage.

What to do

Shallow scratches can be polished out by a process hardly more invasive than the oxidation restoration we've just discussed. Here's how:

- *Start by compounding the scratch and its immediate surrounding area. This will clean the surface and may even remove the scratch! In which case it's job done. If not...*

- *Use a small square of P400 grit wet-or-dry, using it wet and abrading the scratch back by hand with a gentle circular action (see page 14).*

- *Once the scratch has disappeared, extend the patch a little wider, this time with much finer P1000 wet-or-dry, again used wet. Do not let any residue go down the drain.*

- *Finally, compound the whole area to restore the shine and wax polish in the usual way.*

Deeper gouges must be filled with matching gelcoat which has been thickened slightly with colloidal silica. White boats have it relatively easy because tubes of pigmented filler, along with the necessary catalyst in gel form, are commonly available from chandlers. The white may not exactly match the shade on your boat, but it's usually close enough.

For fairly new boats of more striking colour, pre-pigmented matching repair kits can sometimes be obtained from the builders or importers. If not, you will have to add special pigments to clear gelcoat to obtain a match – not easy to do accurately and possibly time to call in the professionals.

Before we move on there are some important facts you should know about polyester gelcoat fillers:

- They shrink on curing – the result of solvents being released from the paste. This means that if you fill a scratch level with the surrounding surface, once cured it will have shrunk back and require filling yet again.

- The surface of polyester gelcoats will remain tacky, no matter how long they are left to cure. This is due to a reaction known as 'air inhibition' and is intentional, allowing subsequent laminates to bond chemically to the gelcoat. When used for fillers this is a disadvantage which can be overcome by adding small quantities of wax – usually supplied dissolved in styrene. During the cure process, the wax rises to the surface and seals it from the air. And no air means no inhibition!

- **MOST IMPORTANT. Read the Warning on this page!**

SKIPPER'S TIP

WARNING!

Polyester resins are cured by adding catalysts. All such catalysts are dangerous. The commonest comprises a dilute solution of 'methyl ethyl ketone peroxide', an organic oxidant which can cause serious skin damage and even blindness if it gets into your eyes. It can also cause substances soaked in it to ignite spontaneously.

When handling the catalyst take extreme care. Wear gloves and safety goggles. Clean up any spillage immediately.

Now let's get on with filling that gouge. You will already have acquired some pigmented gelcoat, thickened to a paste by the addition of colloidal silica – if white then available in a handy prepared form – and containing wax to prevent air inhibition. You will catalyse when you're ready.

Now ...

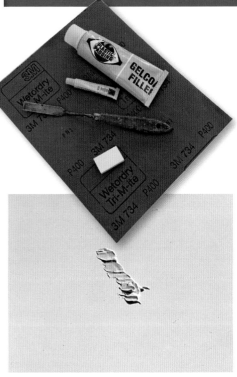

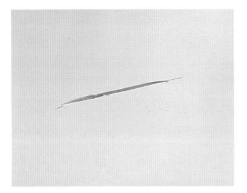

1 *Rake out the gouge, removing any loose fragments, and clean well with acetone. Beware! Acetone is highly flammable.*

2 *Catalyse the filler and mix well. Then fill the gouge with an artist's palette knife or plastic spatula so that it stands a little proud of the surface.*

3 *Once fully hardened, abrade back flush, starting with P400 grit wet-or-dry used wet. A small rubbing block (I use a piece cut from a pencil eraser) can be very useful. For large areas, professionals might use a mechanical sander but the potential to end up with more damage than you started with is high. Unless very confident in your abilities, play safe and do it by hand.*

4 *Once the surface is fair and flat again follow up with P1000 (again used wet) finishing with cutting compound and polish as previously described. The repair should be virtually indiscernible. Collect and dispose of any residue from rubbing down.*

GELCOAT CRAZING

These common defects appear as hairline cracks in the gelcoat and are either caused by impact damage or, more seriously, excessive flexure of the laminate (see Chapter 3). Minor localised impact damage – often known as star crazing, because it radiates from a central point – is usually a relatively minor defect, of very little structural significance. That damage can be caused by either external or internal impact. Typical causes could be a minor collision or, in boats with recessed anchor wells forward, someone stowing the hook with immoderate gusto.

What to do

First make sure the damage really is minor, with no serious damage to the laminate underneath. Take professional advice if necessary.

- *First open up the individual gelcoat cracks, either with a hand tool – perhaps a sharp scriber or the corner of a chisel – or, better still, a small electric rotary file such as that made by Dremel. Think 'dentist' and you'll get the picture.*

- *Repair the cracks in the manner described on the opposite page.*

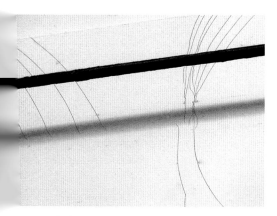

▲ **Gelcoat cracks can arise from a number of different causes. This example is probably from impact.**

THINNING GELCOAT

We touched on this earlier back on page 8. And it's not good news. Pinholes are a sure sign that the gelcoat is nearing the end of its useful life. The endless cycle of weathering and polishing gradually erodes it away, until the tiny air bubbles it contains are exposed (Figure 2.1). A few isolated pinholes are no great cause for concern, but if the gelcoat is extensively peppered, then early action may be advisable.

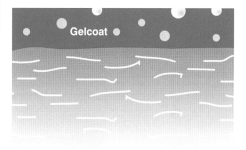

Figure 2.1: Bubbles in the gelcoat will appear as pinholes as the surface wears down.

On paler gelcoats, which have thinned, the darker laminate beneath can often be seen 'shadowing through'. This is best seen in bright sunlight, standing back a few feet, so you can view a largish area at a time.

What to do

- *Further polishing will only exacerbate the problem. Painting the topsides is the only solution – preferably with a two-part polyurethane paint though reasonable durability can be had from using a one-part polyurethane such as Toplac®. Further information on application techniques for two-part paints is included in the Appendix on page 126, though hand painting with two-part paints can be very tricky and is usually best left to the professionals who, anyway, will probably spray it.*

CHAPTER 3

Life below the waterline

When **first introduced,** GRP boats were thought to be nigh on maintenance-free and virtually impervious to the challenges of a life spent partially immersed. And to be fair, they haven't done too badly with many now-elderly examples still giving sterling service – and, what's more, showing every indication of continuing to do so for many years to come.

We now take a more realistic view, acknowledging GRP's undoubted merits, but from the standpoint of having learned a thing or two about its vulnerabilities. The first shocking realisation was that GRP laminates weren't entirely waterproof. Granted, they didn't take on water like their timber-planked forebears, but it became apparent that moisture was penetrating the gelcoat and invading the laminate – at least on a microscopic level.

In short we were rudely confronted by the dreaded 'O' word – osmosis!

OSMOSIS

In the boating context the word has come to mean (in some senses inaccurately) a particular condition, whereas it more accurately describes a process. More specifically, it's the mechanism by which a liquid of lesser viscosity is drawn through a semi-permeable membrane to dilute a liquid of greater viscosity – basically an attempt to equalise the viscosities on both sides. And just in case we believe osmosis always to be destructive, we should remind ourselves that it is essential to life itself. Animals (including us) rely on it to control the fluids in

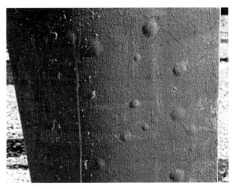

▲ It's almost impossible to keep the water out of moulded GRP rudders, which mean they come under attack from both inside and outside. Unsurprisingly, rudder blades are especially susceptible to osmosis.

our bodies, and plants to extract water and nutrients from the soil.

In the case of a hull, the gelcoat forms the membrane. When a boat is first launched, water passes slowly through it and starts to dissolve loose chemicals – mainly glycols which are strongly hygroscopic, readily attracting the water – and also the polyvinyl-acetate binders used to make some glass reinforcements easy to handle.The combination of the water and chemical solutes (meaning dissolved substances) forms a high-viscosity liquid, and an osmotic cell is born. From here on the process continues inexorably, drawing yet more water from outside to reduce the viscosity within. The result is those splendid blisters we all so love and admire (Figure 3.1).

At this point it's worth referring to

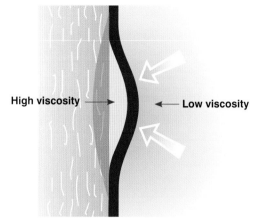

High viscosity ⟶ ⟵ Low viscosity

▲ Figure 3.1

resins of the polyester persuasion. For constructional purposes the normal laminating resins are known as 'orthophthalic'. These were developed first. They have good strength characteristics but are relatively permeable. Up until the late 1980s these were used for both gelcoats and laminating. Then along came 'isophthalic' resins which are just as strong but more resistant to water absorption – and more expensive.

While recognising the attractive qualities of isophthalics, the cost disincentive remained. So a compromise was struck. Isophthalic resins were quickly adopted for gelcoats while the general laminating continued as before. This practice is common to this day.

The upshot of this development is that hulls moulded from the late 1980s onwards are likely to be inherently better protected against the onset of osmosis than those built before.

But don't despair. Unwelcome though it is, osmotic blistering isn't the end of the world. The process advances very slowly and only rarely reaches the point where it becomes structurally detrimental. However, the effect on a boat's value can be dramatic, possibly slashing thousands of pounds off its worth on the open market.

All in all, it's definitely something to avoid. Or rectify.

What to do

The ideal situation would be to protect the hull before it got anywhere near the water but this isn't always practicable. Epoxy resins of the type formulated specifically for hull protection are about six times more impermeable than polyester gelcoats, so could form an effective barrier for new boats if properly applied and of an adequate thickness.

Unfortunately, boat manufacturers are often reluctant to interrupt their production schedules to do this extra work. Also, immature laminates aren't always the best candidates. They may still bear traces of mould-release wax and could contain styrene which has yet to emerge from the laminate. Neither is ideal for the good adhesion of an epoxy coating.

So, some options remain.

- *Take the majority view and do nothing. Antifoul the hull and launch the boat. Face the future with equanimity. It should be at least ten years or so before a problem develops by which time you might have changed boats or – heaven forbid – quit boating.*

- *Use the boat for a couple of seasons. Then have her lifted out in the autumn, lightly grit-blast to remove the antifouling paint and abrade the surface, and allow to dry, ensuring that all blasted matter is collected. Next spring, apply one of the proprietary epoxy protective systems, remembering to follow the manufacturer's recommendations, particularly with regard to the coating thickness.*

- *Wait until a problem appears and deal with it then.*

NOTE: Once osmotic blistering becomes established it can either be ignored or treated – the choice often depending upon the market value of the boat. Full details of recommended treatment processes are in the Technical Appendix on page 128.

SKIPPER'S TIP

INFLUENCING FACTORS

- Due to its lower viscosity, fresh water is more invasive than seawater. This means that a boat on the Thames, say, will probably develop osmotic blisters before one based in the Solent.

- Warm water is more invasive than cold. A boat in the Mediterranean is at greater risk than one in Britain.

- It has been suggested that hard usage will accelerate the onset of blistering. This means a charter boat might develop problems before one used for weekend cruising. Personally, I'm not convinced.

ALL ABOUT ANTIFOULING – OR NEARLY ALL

On page 12 we alluded to the algae that turn our waterlines a shade of nicotine yellow, and this is just one of the examples of how mischievous waterborne inhabitants can torment us. Yet, annoying though the algae are, when it comes to creating drag they are relatively minor players compared to their larger, more assertive playmates.

Many types of underwater organisms, both animal and vegetable, spend most of their life anchored to solid objects. And they're not fussy. They make no real distinction between the rocks and wrecks provided by nature and history and the hulls so considerately donated by boat owners. These maritime squatters are extremely diverse and are also amazing survivors in their exceedingly hostile environment.

Varied though they are, they all share one common knack – the ability to cling on with the most extraordinary tenacity. Let's look at them individually:

Weed

From the plant world we have grasses and seaweeds. These depend on light for photosynthesis so grow on or near the waterline. The underside of a hull is less likely to be affected.

Animals

These divide into two types: hard-bodied creatures such as barnacles, tubeworms and mussels, and soft-bodied hydroids (related to jellyfish) and ascidians such as sea-squirts.

Slime

Here we are talking single-celled micro-organisms that form layers of... well, slime... on underwater surfaces. Ostensibly fragile they might appear but they are not easily dislodged and will reduce the effectiveness of any antifouling they cover.

All of these feed by extracting nutrients from the water, so can actually benefit from the waterflow bestowed by a boat's velocity.

No one likes to be inhospitable but the costs in every sense are too high.

For instance:

- The extra drag and weight slows our boats.

- Encrusted propellers can be rendered virtually useless.

- Rudders can be restricted in the arc through which they turn, thereby limiting your ability to manoeuvre.

- Seacocks can become blocked.

- Instrument transducers can be rendered less effective; log transducers can be put out of action entirely.

- And then – a final irony – we must haul the boat out at regular intervals, first to evict our unwanted tenants and then to take steps against further colonisation.

There's nothing new about this contest between man and fouling agents. The battle raged for centuries without success until relatively recent times. The first significant advance – the use of copper sheeting – was first proposed around 1700 and by the end of that century the Royal Navy had acknowledged its efficacy and had ordered most of its ships clad.

And even today copper remains the first material of choice – though not in a way our ancient mariners would recognise. Two forms are used: cuprous oxide and cuprous thyocianate. The first is the most potent and the second is less galvanically active with aluminium – an important consideration for aluminium boats and other components such as drive legs.

Copper is effective against weed and barnacles but is a poor performer when repelling slime. Other biocides are added to give ultimate protection, with the price penalties one might expect from such refinements.

Conventional antifoulings generally fall into two groups: hard and soft – but there's also a 'thin film' type, almost exclusively used by racing boats because of its ultra-smooth surface.

Let's look at the first two individually:

Hard

Once commonly known as 'hard racing copper' because it can be burnished to produce a smooth surface. As the name implies this is a hard coating of acrylic resin impregnated with the various biocides that are formulated to leach gradually from it over time. Once exhausted, the resin remains and, of course, builds up in thickness over the years.

Soft

This type is also classified as 'erodible' or 'ablative' and describes a coating which wears away due to the friction between itself and the water. As the paint film erodes, fresh biocides are exposed, ready to repel boarders. In theory, once the coating has disappeared, its efficacy is over. In practice, it can become ineffective before all of it is gone. A secondary advantage of soft antifoulings is that they are self-polishing, becoming smoother as they erode. There is much less build-up with this type.

THE POISONED CHALICE

Antifoul performs a function by reducing the growth on the hull, making our vessels more efficient through the water. It is important, however, that no antifoul from washing down is allowed to drain into the watercourse. The concentrated antifoul will have a detrimental effect on the local marine wildlife.

PAINTING HER BOTTOM

Although professional applicators might use airless spray guns, most antifouling is applied with brushes or rollers – often a combination of both, with large, unobstructed areas being rolled on, leaving a brush to do the fiddly bits.

Here's how to go about it:

- If changing brands, check compatibility with the suppliers first. Some combinations need special primers or removal of the existing coating. For example, when applying a hard antifouling over a softer type you may need a primer – often a bituminous one such as Primocon® – or it may even need to be removed entirely. Different manufacturers make different primers so, again, check with them, specifying the coating already on the hull.

- As with all forms of painting, preparation is vital. The surface should be clean and free of last year's fouling growth. If possible, high-pressure clean with fresh water. Any flaking patches of old coatings should be removed with a scraper or similar. Collect and dispose of all dust. Don't forget that you're dealing with toxic substances. Wear gloves, safety goggles and a dust mask.

- Mask off the waterline, choosing the masking tape carefully. If it's all to be done in a single day, the cheap and cheerful type will suffice. If not, use a superior type that won't 'bake on' in UV light. 3M's Scotch-Blue Painter's Tape® is one such example.

- Watch the weather. Rain could ruin your day, as will dew if you start too early. Temperature is also important, with 3–5°C being the absolute minimum.

- Read the manufacturer's instructions carefully. And FOLLOW THEM, particularly

▲ A long-reach pile-type roller is a useful tool for applying antifouling, with a cheap brush to deal with the fiddlier details.

▲ Masking off calls for a good eye and steady hands. If you intend leaving the tape on for more than 24 hours, choose a type that won't 'bake on' to the surface.

regarding the coating thickness. For this you need the 'wetted surface' area, which can be estimated by using the formula shown below.

- *Stir all antifoulings thoroughly before painting. They contain heavy ingredients which rapidly settle in the bottom of the can. In cold conditions you may need some thinners. Usually no more than 10% is recommended. One problem with*

▲ Load the roller with no more than you need. Antifouling is too expensive to waste dripping onto the ground.

HOW MUCH WILL YOU NEED?

You should check the manufacturer's specification but for estimating purposes reckon on 9–10 square metres per litre (m^2/l) per coat.

The underwater area of your hull will depend upon type but, again for estimating purposes, the following formula will give you a guide:

Area = LOA x B x 0.85

Although there are 'one coat' antifoulings on the market, most types require two coats. Resist the temptation to skimp, either by applying the antifouling more thinly or reducing the number of coats.

over-thinning is that it creates the illusion that you've applied more than you actually have. Remember: with antifouling, it's the finished coating thickness that counts.

■ *Actually applying the stuff is somewhat anticlimactic. I like to do the waterline and fiddly bits first before coating the wider expanses. When it comes to that last part, start with the lower reaches and work your way upwards, thus avoiding getting wet antifouling in your hair.*

■ *Try to use a tarpaulin when applying antifoul.*

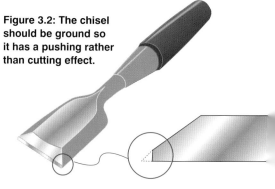

Figure 3.2: The chisel should be ground so it has a pushing rather than cutting effect.

SKIPPER'S TIP

Store your roller and brush overnight by immersing them in a bucket of water. You will find them still soft the following day. Then you should remove the water from the bristles by rolling or brushing against an old plank or similar. A couple of minutes and you're ready to start work again.

ANTIFOULING REMOVAL

Let's start by saying this is one of boat maintenance's least delightful jobs – so unpleasant, I confess, that I've been known to delay the inevitable long after it should have been done.

The options are:

■ Scrape it off dry. Arduous though it is, this can be relatively painless if the antifouling isn't adhering well. Perhaps counter-intuitively, a thick build-up of paint is easier to remove than a thin one. Use a scraper or broad chisel, with its edge ground to the profile shown in Figure 3.2. A few scrape marks to the gelcoat are inevitable. Wear a dust mask and safety glasses or goggles.

■ Use a chemical stripper. Be careful in your choice. Some paint strippers are too aggressive for use on GRP, so check the specification to make sure it's suitable. These strippers usually come in a gel form which is brushed on with a stippling action to build up its thickness. After allowing the antifouling to soften – anything between 1 and 24 hours, depending upon the paint thickness and stripper used – a blunt wooden scraper can be used to remove the softened coating. This is an incredibly messy job so protect yourself accordingly. Heavy, solvent-proof gloves are essential as the stripper can sting your skin. Ditto safety glasses to keep the stuff out of your eyes. This is not a task for the faint-hearted.

■ Grit blasting – wet or dry. Almost always a job for a professional, since it needs expensive equipment. The attraction of taking this route is obvious – you entrust the work to someone else. But, be warned. Although most of the operatives are highly skilled, and know exactly what blasting medium to use and at what pressure, there is always the risk of damage to the gelcoat. If, say, there are voids behind the gelcoat, the blasting could open them up. It could be argued that this is a good thing but that's for you to decide. Certainly, by lightly abrading the surface, blasting does a good job of preparing it for recoating.

■ Always ensure that antifoul removed from the hull is collected and disposed of.

STRESS CRAZING

This is the considerably more serious brother to the minor gelcoat crazing we described on page 15. There's no getting away with it – the sea is a lumpy old place and all boats must be expected to take a hammering in heavy going. Some flexing of a hull shell is both natural and desirable. Within reason it will do no damage, provided that the stresses are absorbed gradually into the yacht's structure as a whole. However, if this benign flexing is abruptly restricted by structural 'hard spots', then the material can fatigue and, in due course, could fail.

Such hard spots are usually caused by the boat's internal structure – bulkheads, soles, bunk bases, et cetera. A common situation is illustrated in Figure 3.3. Here, a thin plywood bulkhead is bonded directly to the inside surface of the hull shell. Forward and aft of the bulkhead, the hull flexes within its elastic limits, comfortably absorbing the buffeting of the waves. But that narrow, unyielding edge brings all movement to an abrupt halt, generating an immense concentration of stress along the line where the bulkhead abuts the hull.

Planing-type power boats, with their low deadrise hulls, are especially prone to this form of damage. I have seen hulls cracked right through, along the line of a bulkhead, as neatly as if someone had taken a saw to it.

Note that if you own a high-speed single-screw powerboat, the side most prone to damage will be that lying opposite to the prop's rotation. That's to say that if the prop rotates to the right, the port side of the hull will be pressed down. Such a boat could land very heavily on that side if, say, it jumped off a wave. Needless to say, the damage usually occurs below the waterline but can extend into the topsides.

If the stress crazing is limited to a fairly small area, then repair can be both easy and effective. But if much of the internal structure appears to be struggling to break through to the outside, then either the boat has suffered a serious accident – a grounding or collision, perhaps – or it has to be assumed that the boat is just badly designed, a discouraging conclusion. Quite apart from the structural implications, cracks below the waterline provide a ready path for water to enter the laminate – never a good idea.

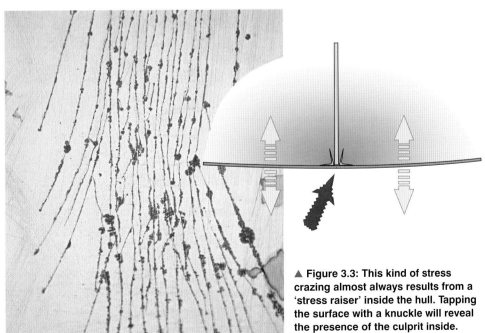

▲ Figure 3.3: This kind of stress crazing almost always results from a 'stress raiser' inside the hull. Tapping the surface with a knuckle will reveal the presence of the culprit inside.

What to do

■ First take advice, either from a surveyor or trustworthy shipwright. Although sometimes described as 'gelcoat' crazing, it's likely that the damage actually extends deeper into the laminate itself and there may even be some delamination of the layers of GRP which won't be visible from the surface. Where there are structural problems, simply filling the surface cracks would be a pointless exercise, achieving nothing. The cracks would almost certainly reappear when the panel flexes again in service (See page 45).

■ The affected areas should be ground right back to sound laminate (deeper than the cracks or delamination) and the GRP made good in proper fashion. There may also be some internal work required to ensure the defect doesn't emerge again.

■ Finally, of course, the gelcoat must be restored by filling, fairing and polishing.

■ Unless you are very confident of your skills, this is definitely a job for the professional.

■ If the damage occurred because of a basic design fault, it will be likely to recur if steps are not taken to correct that fault. This could be, say, modification of the internal structure to remove a stress concentration, or perhaps using a more flexible resin (see panel below) able to absorb those stresses. For more radical remedial action, see Chapter 7.

SKIPPER'S TIP

STRETCHED TO THE LIMIT

The marriage between polyester resins and glass fibres is generally a good one but there are incompatibilities. Of relevance to stress crazing is the difference in a nerdy characteristic known as 'elongation to break'. This defines how far (in percentage terms) a material can be stretched before it fails.

Whereas glass fibres might stretch as much as 5 per cent, the polyester resin that binds them is only capable of about 3 per cent. It's hardly surprising then that the resin fails before the glass reinforcements – exactly what happens with many instances of stress crazing.

Epoxies and vinylesters, on the other hand, are much more elastic with stretch characteristics well into double figures and far in excess of glass reinforcements.

CHAPTER 4

Decks

In one respect at least, decks live a less enviable life than the topsides. In addition to the weathering effects of sunlight and rain, they must endure people tramping over them, sometimes wearing grit-laden shoes. It's not always appreciated that, even at sea, abrasive particles fall from the sky. For instance, the southerly siroccos of the Mediterranean bring what's known colloquially as 'red rain', the colour being due to fine sand carried from the Sahara. I've even known it fall in the West Indies, having crossed the Atlantic borne on the trade winds. And then, of course, there are always volcanic ash clouds which can encircle the entire globe before falling to earth again. Although the particles are tiny, volcanic dust is very hard and abrasive – a significant threat to jet engines which

accidentally ingest it and not exactly friendly towards decks.

GELCOAT VOIDS

Compared to hulls with their smoothly curved surfaces, GRP decks are relatively complex, comprising numerous angular planes and the associated edges and corners where those planes meet. For the laminator they present more of a challenge than hulls and – human fallibility being what it is – unsurprisingly, they are more prone to moulding defects.

Perhaps the most common are gelcoat voids – basically pockets of trapped air where the laminate was poorly consolidated behind the gelcoat. Back in Chapter 1 we outlined the basic moulding procedure where individual components were moulded in

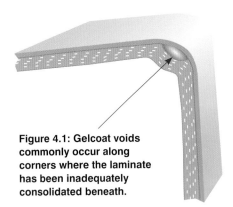

Figure 4.1: Gelcoat voids commonly occur along corners where the laminate has been inadequately consolidated beneath.

female moulds. The result of this process is that the mould's 'inside' corners become 'outside' corners in the actual moulding. And it just happens that one of the trickier tasks facing the laminators is to ensure the laminate is pressed firmly into all those nooks and crannies. A moment's carelessness can easily result in a gelcoat void (Figure 4.1).

Irritating though they are, the good news is that they are structurally insignificant and can easily be repaired as described on page 14.

CORE SEPARATION

Sometimes known as 'delamination', but that's a somewhat shotgun term used to describe a host of sometimes unrelated defects.

Core separation

With decks, the problem arises from the characteristics of glassfibre itself. As a material it's immensely strong but not very stiff. To gain the necessary stiffness from a solid laminate for, say, the cabin top or side decks would make it unacceptably

heavy. So designers often introduce a lightweight 'core' to increase the thickness – and thereby stiffness – without the weight penalty. Core materials vary: 'end-grain' balsa or closed cell foam being popular choices, less commonly plywood.

To understand the potential problem, we must again go back to the moulding process. The deck is moulded upside down. Immediately after the gelcoat has hardened comes the laminate that will eventually form the top of the deck. While that laminate is still 'wet' – meaning the resin is still in its liquid state – the core is pressed down onto it, with the laminator doing what he can to squeeze out the air from underneath. Unfortunately, since the core is opaque and any voids therefore invisible, complete success can't be guaranteed.

Signs of core separation include:

- Springiness or softness underfoot – the trampoline symptom. If a deck is firm on one side and soft in the same area on the other side, fear the worst.
- Creaking sounds as you walk along the deck. There other possible explanations so don't panic yet.
- Obvious depressions in the deck. If the core is end-grain balsa or plywood, it could have rotted.

What to do

- *There are no easy fixes. The moisture content of the deck should be measured by a surveyor to see if water has penetrated – and, if so, how far. If the problem is minor and the core not susceptible to rot – i.e. synthetic – often the best course is to ignore it.*

- *However, if the phrase 'rotten to the core' applies, more radical action could be necessary. If the affected area is known to be dry, it may be possible simply to inject an epoxy resin though small holes drilled into the void from above.*

■ If wet and thought to be rotten, balsa or plywood cores will need removal and you should definitely seek the advice of a professional. The precise remedy will depend on the circumstances but one method is to use a circular 'hole saw' to remove closely spaced discs (sometimes called 'biscuits') from the upper skin. This is followed by raking out the core and making good the deck – a very considerable job.

GETTING A GRIP

The majority of modern boats' decks have non-slip textures moulded into the various walkways. Some are more effective than others but few as grippy as the other options. So...

Dealing with moulded decks

GRP decks can be treated in much the same way as the topsides – with one important exception. NEVER WAX THEM. You might think the reasons for this self-evident but it's astonishing how many owners spend time burnishing their decks into an enviable shine, only to find them converted into skating rinks. A smidgeon of extra lustre is never worth the risk of somebody becoming an MOB statistic.

Other non-slip materials

Deck paint: A firm favourite for many years but now considered rather old-fashioned. There are different options within this group.

■ The first is a mix of fairly conventional paints (alkyds, occasionally chlorinated rubber) to which a 'matting agent' has been added to remove the shine. For yet more grip, larger particles are introduced to produce an even rougher surface. Both grades are readily available and can be applied like normal paint.

Sand was the original particle material of choice but proved too aggressive to clothing and human flesh alike. Modern deck paints are more likely to use miniscule polyethylene beads (or another plastic) or even such substances as finely ground nut shells.

■ Two-part polyurethane paints (never epoxy, which is more susceptible to UV attack) can also be used, first adding the matting agent, then sprinkling on

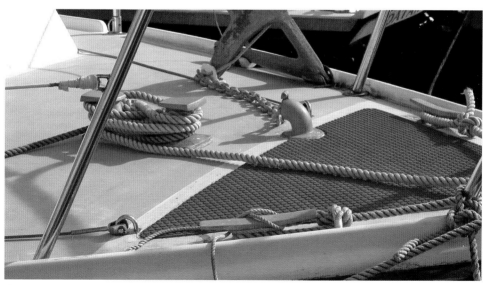

▲ Two forms of non-slip surfacing on the same foredeck: Treadmaster®, a patterned cork compound sheeting, and light blue alkyd-based deck paint.

SKIPPER'S TIP

Ideally, non-slip areas should be of a contrasting colour to the moulding beneath so the areas where it's safest to stand are obvious, even in low-light conditions. The modern practice of monotone mouldings, where there's no clear distinction between slick and rough surfaces is, in my opinion, an economy too far.

the particles until you have an efficient non-slip surface. Cured polyurethanes are very slippery with a film of water over them, so be careful not to leave any shiny patches.

Care of painted decks

■ *Simply wash down occasionally. None except the two-part polyurethanes are very hard-wearing, so periodic repainting should be anticipated.*

Stick-on non-slip sheeting

These can be made of a rubberised cork compound (Treadmaster®) or of flexible polyurethane sheeting (TBS®) stuck down onto the walkways with various types of adhesives. The non-slip properties of these materials is usually excellent, though wear can diminish their efficacy. Some can be restored by over-coating with paints specially formulated for the purpose.

Care of non-slip sheeting

■ *Wash as before. Another task you may face is to stick down any edges or corners that start to lift. Your choice of adhesive will depend on whatever was used originally – epoxy or polyurethane sealant being the commonest choice but it's important to try and remove any dirt from underneath before you start.*

TROUBLES WITH TEAK

Here we're referring to unvarnished, exterior teak – with a particular focus on teak decks. The more decorative, varnished teak we'll be dealing with shortly.

Teak is a tropical hardwood, part of

the *Lamiaceae* family, rather implausibly related to mint. It originates from S.E. Asia – still its main source – but is now grown commercially (and sustainably) elsewhere.

Teak's principal attraction for marine use is its durability. It contains oils and other chemical compounds that give it an exceptional degree of natural protection. Another characteristic is a high fibre content which makes it both elastic and resistant to abrasion. All in all, the perfect timber for exterior joinerwork.

But at a cost, since it has never been a cheap material. What most of us know as teak decks are relatively thin strips laid onto a moulded GRP substrate. 10–12mm-thick planks can be considered luxurious, 6–8mm is more common and the cheapest decks are hardly more than a miserly veneer on a plywood base.

Teak's potential downfall lies in the fact that it takes on a dull shade of grey when weathered. Many consider it unsightly and the impulse to do something about it is strong. Unfortunately the consequent damage can be severe. In common with all timbers, teak has a grain – the outcome of the tree's annular growth rings. Hard and soft densities alternate, mirroring the seasonal variations in growth rate due to

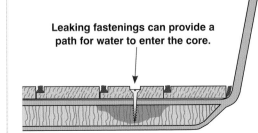

Leaking fastenings can provide a path for water to enter the core.

summer cold versus winter warmth, or parched and rainy seasons. The upshot of this inconsistency is that, when scrubbed hard, the softer material gets scoured away fastest leaving prominent ridges in the planking.

What to do

Tough it might be, but teak must be treated gently. NEVER USE A CONVENTIONAL SCRUBBING BRUSH OR A POWER JET CLEANER.

- *The best tool is either a sponge-type mop or a very soft deck brush with 'feathered' bristles. Always sponge across the grain – NEVER along the grain.*

- *As a cleaning fluid use a strong detergent dissolved in water – preferably fresh water, but I've had good results with clean sea water heaved in from over the side.*

- *If the teak is badly soiled or stained, follow the detergent with an application of one of the proprietary teak cleaners containing oxalic acid. Follow the manufacturer's instruction and be patient. Bleaches take time to work.*

- *Rinse off well once you're satisfied.*

Signs that the teak is seriously worn are the grain ridges mentioned earlier, and fastenings becoming visible on the surface. Another indicator can often be found where the planking abuts vertical components like hatch coamings and cabin sides – places where the original thickness can be seen.

Whether or not the situation can be redeemed without replacing the planking will depend upon its thickness. Let's assume for now that enough material remains to eke a few more years' service from it.

What to do

The ridges can be reduced in prominence with a belt sander – though this is something

▲ **Badly worn and weathered teak. The paying is pulling away from the sides of the seams and the teak plug is missing from one of the fastenings.**

you should only consider as something of a last resort. It's not necessary to sand the planking down until it's absolutely flat – indeed, it's arguable that some unevenness improves its non-slip properties. But even a partial reduction will improve its appearance. In contrast to the cleaning procedure, the sander should be operated along the grain, since cross-grained sanding can pull out the 'caulking'. (Actually the correct term is 'paying'. Caulking is more correctly the act of tamping in strands of cotton or oakum to help fill gaps in planking. The paying is the final injection of a sealing material such as pitch or – these days – a synthetic polymer such as polysulphide or polyurethane.)

Talking of which...

Payed seams tend to break down with time. The classic symptom is to find the rubbery compound pulling away from the side of grooves. Whether or not to instigate repairs is a matter of degree. Most of us would ignore minor indications, perhaps postponing radical repairs until the problem becomes more advanced.

Is this wise? Well, that depends upon the construction of the deck. If the laminate has a balsa core then there's always the chance that water could migrate through the seam, down through a screw-hole and into the core. As we covered on page 26 balsa is both absorbent and non-durable.

SKIPPER'S TIP

TO MASK OR NOT TO MASK?

Opinions vary. Some shipwrights accept the inevitable spill-over and simply sand it all away once the sealing compound is cured. Others prefer to minimise the mess by running masking tape up each side of the seam.

The decision can depend on the thickness of the teak. If it is very thin and you're reluctant to sand it back heavily then opt for masking tape. If so, the tape should be moved when the sealant is partially cured – a matter of surprisingly fine judgement, always with the risk of pulling away the sealant. Better slightly too early than too late.

And damp, unventilated spaces, warmed from above by the sun, provide the ideal environment for rot.

What to do

There's only one thing for it – the seams must be raked out, cleaned, and re-payed. The professionals might use a router, which will make short work of the task, but this is a high-risk operation, not recommended for the unskilled. Routers have all the directional waywardness of supermarket trolleys and the potential for damage is considerable.

It's much safer but slower to do it by hand:

■ First run a craft knife down the sides of each seam, separating any sealant that's still adhering to the timber.

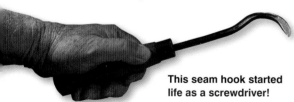

This seam hook started life as a screwdriver!

■ Next use a 'seam hook' (or 'seam rake'), usually a bent-over screwdriver, a little narrower than the seam and sharpened into a beak-like edge, to rake out the sealant. This has to be done carefully, taking care not to damage the sides of the seam.

■ Remove all debris – a vacuum cleaner being useful here – and prime the seam with whichever primer is recommended

for your choice of sealant. Allow the primer to dry for about 30 minutes.

■ Run 'seam breaker' (also known as 'bond breaker') tape down the bottom, horizontal face of each seam (see below). This prevents three-side bonding which will hasten the failure of the seam.

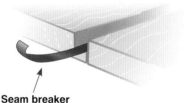

Seam breaker

■ Refill the seams with a polysulphide or polyurethane sealing compound to a level just above the surface. Smooth it down lightly with a spatula – don't apply too much pressure.

■ Allow to cure – a matter of some days, depending upon conditions and the particulars of the product – then use a belt or sander to abrade the excess away – sanding along the seam, never across it. Don't varnish or oil the deck for at least 30 days.

To repair small areas of damaged seam, make diagonal cuts and remove the defective sealant carefully.

CHAPTER 5

Painting and varnishing

PAINTS

With the exception of antifouling and non-slip deck coatings, paints don't feature much on modern boats – at least in their more youthful days, though of course they are often used to refurbish senior examples of the species. But paint still has a place in minor roles: cove bands, boot stripes, sign-writing, et cetera. Many paint jobs don't call for professional knowledge or equipment, so are usually well within the capabilities of boat owners.

The paint systems we are most familiar with can be grouped into two categories:

- **One-part paints:** These are the easiest to use and are usually alkyd resin based or alkyd modified with polyurethane.

- **Two-part paints:** Primers can be two-part epoxies but, to take advantage of their UV resistance, the finish coats are invariably two-part polyurethanes. The primers are relatively easy to handle but two-part polyurethane topcoats demand skills and facilities that may be beyond most DIYers (See Appendix, page 126).

Preparation

As usual, preparation is the key to achieving a satisfactory result. Indeed, if you do the job properly – as I'm sure you will! – expect to find yourself spending perhaps 80 per cent of the time 'prepping' the surface and only 20 per cent wielding a paintbrush.

Before you start you should know that...

- If an existing paint system is cracking, peeling or showing any signs of flaking away, it should be removed completely. Remember that a coating's adhesion can only be as good as whatever lies beneath it.

- The surface must be clean of all contaminants – including wax polishes. There are dedicated pre-painting cleaners formulated specially for the task.

- The surface must be abraded to provide a 'key' for the new coating. This can be done by hand, using 180–200 grade abrasive paper, but a less strenuous alternative is to use either an orbital or random orbit electric sander.

The tools for the job

Brush: There's nothing more infuriating than a brush that sheds its bristles so buy the best quality you can lay your hands on. Undercoats are fairly tolerant but gloss paints require long, flexible bristles. Opinions differ between the optimum width. My own choice would be a 2in (50mm) brush but some painters advocate larger.

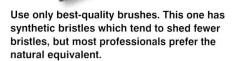

Use only best-quality brushes. This one has synthetic bristles which tend to shed fewer bristles, but most professionals prefer the natural equivalent.

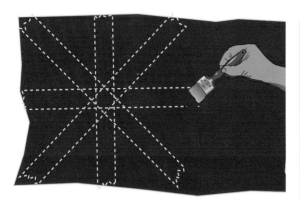

The 'union jack' painting pattern helps guarantee even coverage

- Opinions also vary about the best way to apply paint, but all agree that it should be with a combination of horizontal, vertical, and diagonal strokes – sometimes referred to as the 'union jack' method.

- The most critical stage is the last one – lightly 'laying off' (or 'tipping off') to produce that final gleaming shine. Some recommend the laying off strokes be vertical, others prefer horizontal. The method that works best for me is to lay off horizontally, each stroke being made into the 'wet edge' – meaning the area of still wet paint just previously applied.

- When painting the topsides, work downwards from the gunwale to the waterline in vertical 'drops' about 600-700mm wide.

Brush and roller: Choose your brush as before. For one-part paints a small-cell foam roller is the best choice to accompany it. Again, go for quality. Never use a pile type roller, since it will shed fibres into your finish.

- With two implements to control, it follows that this is really a two person job, though a skilled operator can get by without a helpmate. The roller spreads the paint evenly – and not too vigorously, since this can cause bubbling – and the brusher lays it off immediately, again brushing in towards the wet edge. It takes some coordination, but at least you should have the opportunity to perfect your technique on the less crucial undercoat.

Note: The brusher should resist the temptation to dip his brush into the paint tray. It's the roller's job to keep the supply adequate.

PAINT DAY!

Right. The area to be painted has been prepared and masked off. Here are some things you need to be wary of:

- *If working outside, consult the weather forecast and make sure that there's no chance of rain or strong winds which can raise dust. If the ground is very dusty, it might be worth dampening it with a watering can – at least for the gloss coats.*

- *The ideal conditions are overcast but*

SKIPPER'S TIP

RUNS AND CURTAINS

One of the most tricky challenges to any painter is to judge how much paint to apply. Slap on too much and there will be 'runs' and 'curtains', where the weight of the paint film is more than it will support. Spread the paint too thin and the gloss won't form properly, the surface looking dry with prominent 'drag' marks.

It's important not to overload brushes and rollers. Never dip more than a brush's tip in the paint and always ensure that a roller is evenly loaded by working it on the ramp of the paint tray. It's impossible to be specific. Most people learn by experience – first with the undercoats and finally with those all-important coats of gloss.

▲ Pair painting – often called 'roll and tip'. As you can see the achievable finish can be very impressive.

dry. Direct sunlight should be avoided, particularly when painting dark substrates where the surface temperature can cause paint solvents to evaporate too quickly. Depending on the orientation of the boat, it's sometimes possible to paint one side in the morning and the other in the afternoon.

■ The ambient temperature affects drying and overcoat times – you should check the manufacturer's specification for details. One-part paints are generally tolerant in this regard, but there's a limit to what they can be asked to do.

■ Be mindful of 'dewpoint'. As the day cools, the temperature may drop to a level where it can no longer hold the water vapour contained within it. At that point, the vapour will condense and dew will be formed – the ruination of many an otherwise good paint job. Expect problems when you have high humidity and plunging evening temperatures.

■ Before you start painting, the surface must be dust free. Start with a soft household brush then go over the surface again with a 'dust wipe' – often called a 'tack rag' – a slightly sticky cloth that will remove the smallest particles. On large jobs you may want to do this in stages, advancing just forward of the working area as you go round the boat.

■ Stir the paint well – more thoroughly than you might believe necessary. Many of a paint's most important ingredients will sink to the bottom of the tin and must be properly distributed before you begin.

Finally, it's very important to comply with the manufacturer's recommendations.

Many paint jobs are less magnificent than they might have been because the painter believed he knew better.

But, in particular...

- Use the right thinners and don't exceed the recommended amount. An over-thinned paint will look dull and lifeless.

- Respect the overcoat times. These are temperature related and are intended to allow the solvents sufficient time to evaporate. Resist the temptation to apply two coats in a day when there's really only time for one. Patience is the key.

- Follow the recommended sequence of coatings, any primers and undercoats included and don't skimp. When painters talk of 'depth of shine' they know how it was achieved.

VARNISHES

It's tempting to think of varnish as paint without pigment, and to some extent this is true. However, varnishes are susceptible to one challenge that paints are inherently resistant to. Paint is opaque whereas varnish is transparent, meaning that the latter is subject to UV attack throughout its depth – though most contain additives to combat the effects. Despite these measures, varnishes are generally less durable than paints.

Types of varnish include....

- **Traditional:** These have been around for many hundreds of years and are based on natural oils that dry and harden at normal temperatures. Linseed oil can be used but the best performer is tung oil – unsurprisingly from the nut of the tung tree. These varnishes are easy to use but are soft and easily damaged. On the plus side they are also easily repaired with the occasional 'touch up'.

- **One-part synthetic:** These are derived from alkyd resins but can also be fortified with polyurethanes. They represent the bulk of everyday varnishes most of us use on our boats.

- **Two-part polyurethane:** These are very closely related to two-part polyurethane paints and share their generally high performance characteristics and superior durability. However, they are intolerant of the moisture naturally contained in timber, and are therefore best used over epoxy-sealed surfaces. Being resistant to chemical attack, once cured they are difficult to strip off.

If anything, preparation is even more important with varnishes than it is with paint. Because of its transparency, any flaws will be visible – perhaps even more conspicuous – through the film.

The first step is to decide whether the varnish can be repaired or not. The softer the varnish type, the easier it is to get a satisfactory result by lightly rubbing down the damaged areas with 120–180 grit abrasive paper and gently touching up using a soft-bristled brush and un-thinned varnish. You may decide this is worth a shot anyway. After all, if your attempts fail and you have to strip back to bare wood, it will only have cost you an hour or so of your time.

But let's assume the varnish's condition is beyond any trivial tinkering. It's time to go back to bare wood and start again. Here's how to go about it:

- *For removing varnish, there's only one option – a chemical paint stripper. Make sure you use a type that's GRP friendly – i.e. won't attack surrounding gelcoat – and follow the instructions to the letter. Never leave strippers on longer than necessary. It's usually better to use multiple coats than wait longer than recommended, since even the gentlest*

▲ **Varnish is inherently susceptible to UV attack. Note how the more exposed upper surface has suffered the most.**

products may do damage if in contact with the gelcoat for long enough. Also, partially softened varnish can dry and harden if left too long. Above all, NEVER use hot air guns or gas torches, since these are almost certain to scorch the wood and leave unsightly marks that will show through the coating.

Varnishing new wood or freshly stripped surfaces

■ *Sand the wood (small areas by hand) with 80–180, then 280 grit paper, working in the direction of the grain or at no more than at 45° to it. NEVER sand across the grain because abrasion marks will show through.*

■ *Dust off the surface and wipe clean with whatever thinner is recommended for the varnish type. If varnishing teak, also degrease the surface with acetone or a proprietary acetone-based degreaser. (Note: acetone will not damage surrounding gelcoat.)*

■ *Typical coating schedules appear in the table below but, typically, the first coat should be thinned by up to 30 per cent*

Traditional varnishing schedule

Thinned	No. of coats	Recoat interval		Thinners
		10°C	20°C	
Up to 30 per cent	1	12h – 4d	6h – 2d	No.1
Up to 20 per cent	1	12h – 4d	6h – 2d	No.1
Up to 5 per cent except last coat	4+	12h – 4d	6h – 2d	No.1

(using the recommended thinners) to get good penetration into the timber.

■ *It's important to allow the recommended overcoat time to elapse. These times are temperature dependent and allow the solvents to evaporate to an acceptable level. Typical recommendations are shown in the table.*

■ *The second coat should also be thinned – 10–20 per cent being common.*

■ *The finishing topcoats can also be thinned, but by no more than 5 per cent. If the varnish is still too thick to be workable, it's either too old or the conditions are too cold.*

■ *The finishing coats – 3–4 being the absolute minimum – should be applied with a good-quality brush, working systematically along the piece. Varnishing takes skill so it pays to start on the least conspicuous areas first, leaving the pride and joys till last. As with paint, the objective is to apply just enough for the liquid to 'flow out' without sagging or running. Observe overcoat times. Don't be tempted to hurry the process.*

■ *As you approach the final coat, you should lightly sand the surface (280 grit) to remove 'nibs' and other blemishes (insects being a particular bane). Be patient. It's said that you should apply as many coats as you can afford but this is up to you. It could take as many as ten to get a truly exemplary shine.*

SKIPPER'S TIPS

CARE OF BRUSHES

■ **Use only good-quality brushes and preferably those that have been 'broken in' – meaning those that have been carefully used before and won't shed bristles. Professional painters cherish their brushes and treat them with great care, saving the best for the final coat.**

■ **Never leave them standing in a jar of thinners – not even overnight. The brush's weight will distort the bristles making it unusable. If you need to take a short break – say no more than an hour or two – wrap the bristles in cling film and lay the brush flat on a dust-free surface.**

■ **At the end of the day, wash the brush out thoroughly in the appropriate thinners (No.1 being typical for conventional varnishes) then use warm water and soap to remove any residues. Place the brush somewhere warm (but not hot) where it can dry naturally – again making sure that the bristles are not distorted.**

■ **When using thinners, never dispose of them down a surface water drain as this will lead to the marina or water body.**

CHAPTER 6

Dealing with deck fittings

▲ Not all running rigging is as complicated as this but even the simplest yacht has plenty to take care of.

There's something rather perverse about taking expensive and often intricate bits of kit and then leaving them out in all the horrors nature can throw at them. But that's exactly what we do with our deck fittings. Such essential gear should inspire sympathy not neglect. However, many of us – myself included – become all too accustomed to things looking after themselves and perhaps aren't fully aware of the reality: that they're almost certainly deteriorating.

Let's take a stroll around the deck.

STANCHIONS AND GUARDWIRES

Considering their importance to our safety, neglect here is downright dangerous. Yet surveyors regularly report on the perilous condition of these eminently observable defences.

A typical guardwire system comprises a row of stanchions running down each side deck, terminating fore and aft at the pulpit and stern rail (pushpit, taffrail). Strung along the stanchions you will find a pair of guardwires, one at the top and the other at mid-height. These are almost invariably of stainless steel wire, often sheathed in PVC to reduce chafe and make them easier to see in the dark. The guardwires are tensioned, either by rigging screws, bottlescrews (turnbuckles) or braided polyester lanyards.

The stanchions and their sockets are either aluminium alloy or stainless steel or a combination of both. The sockets are sometimes integral with the toe-rail system, in which case they are invariably of aluminium.

So, you might have:

- Stainless steel stanchion in a stainless steel socket. This is the best arrangement, rarely giving problems.

- Aluminium stanchion in aluminium socket. Very common but potentially the most troublesome combination. Corrosion can build up within the socket forming oxide deposits that are bulkier than the metal they replace. The expansion can – and if neglected often does – crack the socket.

- Aluminium stanchion in stainless steel socket or vice-versa – an unlikely combination since it introduces the additional issue of galvanic corrosion. Stainless steel sockets should be strong enough to resist bursting pressures though aluminium ones are as susceptible as before. On some designs you will find pulpit and stern rail feet secured in aluminium sockets.

This aluminium base was the worst of six cracked ones found during a survey.

What to do

- *Make regular checks that the stanchions have not grown into their sockets. At the first sign, lift the stanchion out and remove all corrosion deposits. Take a few wraps of PTFE tape around the base of the stanchion before replacing.*

▲ Lanyard

- *Tensioning lanyards should be replaced periodically – long before they reach the lamentable condition of that shown in the photograph, below left.*

- *Never use split rings to retain any clevis pins. They can be snatched out by flogging ropes, as is almost the case with the one shown left.*

HAND AND GRAB RAILS

There should be no need to emphasise the importance of these vital aids to safety. Anybody who has worked their way forward along a heaving deck will have either blessed or cursed them, depending on how thoughtfully they have been placed.

Since our lives could depend on them, of course we can take their security for granted. Or can we? My own confidence was shaken when I was involved in the repair of a yacht from a well-regarded Scandinavian yard. A teak handrail had cracked and the owner wanted it replaced. The shipwright entrusted with the job had searched for the fastenings below and not found them. So I decided to phone the importer for some technical advice.

'Oh, no,' I was told, 'there are no bolts. They're just screwed on with self-tapping screws. It only takes a few minutes to change them.'

This is an extreme example but a more common ploy is the use of 'tapping plates' – metal plates (often aluminium) into which threaded holes can be 'tapped' to receive fastenings from outside. While certainly an improvement on self-tapping screws, as we saw with stanchions, the combination of stainless steel and aluminium isn't a particularly happy one in the presence of

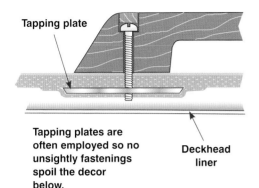

Tapping plate

Tapping plates are often employed so no unsightly fastenings spoil the decor below.

Deckhead liner

salt water. The aluminium corrodes, the fitting becomes insecure, and the only remedy is to do what should have been done in the first place – run bolts through the deck with honest nuts and washers below to ensure the grab rail never comes away in one's hand.

The truth is that we put our trust in the judgement of others, perhaps sometimes misguidedly. It's impossible to be specific as what you should do but two points might help:

■ If a handrail feels insecure it **IS** insecure and almost certainly unsafe. The problem should be rectified immediately.

■ If during completion of the above work you have doubts about the original attachment method, seriously consider doing it another way, taking advice if necessary. Bolting right through the deck leaves no room for doubt.

WINCHES

A winch manufacturer once told me a story. A circumnavigating couple visited his stand at a boat show to tell him how well his winches had performed – welcome praise indeed from folk who had spent over twelve years circling the globe.

'Mind you,' the bloke said as he was about to leave, 'they are getting a bit stiff now. I think we might need replacements before we set off again.'

Torn between the prospect of a sale

and an instinct to defend his product, our manufacturer asked them how often they serviced their winches.

There was a long pause and a bit of foot shuffling. 'Well, actually... not very often,' confessed the male of the species, clearly embarrassed by the question.

'He means never,' said his wife. 'They just kept going so he never got round to it.' A couple of minutes later they were on their way, a complimentary service kit clutched in his hand.

A few days later, the manufacturer got a phone call, thanking him for his advice and support and telling him that just a few hours' work had restored the winches to as youthful condition as they could recall.

The reality is that winches are generally long-lived but they do need at least occasional attention to keep them operating efficiently.

Now, of course, there's no such thing as a standard winch, but there are similarities between most makes. If you don't have the servicing instructions for the winches on your boat, they can probably be obtained from the manufacturers or, more conveniently, downloaded from the internet.

▲ **Servicing details differ from winch to winch. Ensure you have all the information for your own winches.**

SKIPPER'S TIP

Such components as pawls have springs, which mean they are more than capable of flicking themselves impishly over the side. If working in an exposed place – a cockpit coaming being a notable example – a good wheeze is to take a largish cardboard box, deeper than the height of the winch, and cut a hole in its base just a little bigger than the diameter of the winch. Place the box over the winch (if necessary tape it in place) and draw the drum off from above.

A little awkward? Yes, but if anything makes a bid for freedom, there's a good chance of catching it in the box.

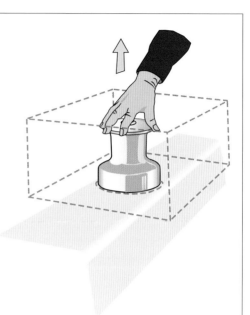

WINDLASSES

Much the same applies to windlasses, but not all are easy to service. The windlass world divides into two types, both manual and electric (or hydraulic on larger models):

- **Horizontal axis** – Once the most common, these are also the most mechanically complex and generally the least easy to service. Their popularity arose from the fact that they allow long cranking handles to be used – the

▲ Horizontal axis windlasses are inherently more mechanically complex than the vertical axis variety.

mechanical advantage gained being important when hauling the rode up by hand.

The internal mechanisms utilise gears or chains and sprockets, with the components often being made of steel – usually encased in a sealed oil bath for lubrication and protection. Casings are usually of cast aluminium with stainless steel fastenings. Galvanic corrosion between the two metals can make them difficult to disassemble.

- **Vertical axis** – The inherent simplicity of this type makes them ideal for electrical power but not for manual operation, which is usually by means of a standard winch handle. To say that the short (10in) length of the handle and the absence of internal gearing makes weighing anchor a bit of a struggle can be an understatement. Acceptable as a backup but, on anything other than the smallest yachts, regard it as a form of job creation for chiropractors.

▲ **This vertical axis windlass is electrically powered and can be dismantled in minutes. Note the snubber that takes the loads off the windlass when at anchor.**

Although some aluminium models are made, most are made from stainless steel or chromed bronze. This means that their above-deck mechanisms are easily stripped for maintenance with very basic tools.

Care of windlasses

The good news is that minimal maintenance usually suffices. Idleness is the enemy – by which I mean the windlass's not the skipper's. So...

■ *Operate your windlass frequently and it will rarely give trouble. If a horizontal axis windlass stands idle for long enough, the oil can drain from the gears and – especially if of steel – they could corrode.*

■ *Wash the windlass down at regular intervals, preferably with fresh water and after every trip.*

■ *Strip the above-deck components down as far as is practicable, following the manufacturer's recommendations. Grease where appropriate but NOT the faces of any clutches or brake bands.*

■ *Regularly inspect any electrics, including the connections below and the foot switches on deck. Make sure the hinged caps are functional, since accidental operation of a windlass can be dangerous.*

If the windlass is powered by its own service battery, check its condition and electrolyte levels (if possible). Pay particular attention to the connections here. Windlasses draw heavy currents and any extra resistance or electrical discontinuity will be sorely felt. If there's any sign of corrosion around the connection posts, disconnect, clean them thoroughly, then protect with a smear of grease once they're reconnected.

But it's more than just maintenance that will keep a windlass in good health. How you use it is also important. Treat it respectfully and it will serve you well.

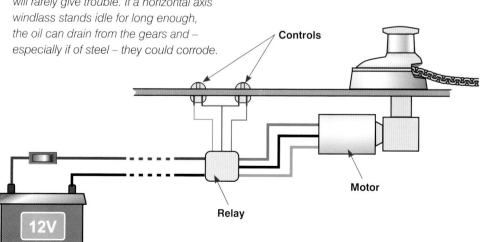

For instance:

- *When at anchor, don't allow the windlass to take all the load. Use a snubber to transfer the load to a mooring cleat. (See previous page.)*

- *Use the engine to help the windlass when weighing anchor. Particularly in a strong tide or wind, motor towards the anchor so the windlass isn't struggling by itself.*

- *Then, if the anchor doesn't break out smartly, put the snubber back on the rode and jerk the anchor out with the engine. Once free, the windlass can continue doing its work.*

- *NEVER let the windlass motor labour for more than a very few seconds. It will overheat and – you can bet on it – early failure is guaranteed.*

BLOCKS, TRACKS AND CLUTCHES

It's good news time again. The general run of deck gear needs very little attention at all, apart from the occasional sluice down with fresh water to remove dirt and grit from their bearing surfaces.

But this is a field where there have been huge technical developments. It used to be thought that exotic gear stuffed with ball and roller bearings belonged exclusively in the world of racing. But, when you think about it, this is illogical. Racing yachts tend to have large crews – and athletic ones at that – whereas cruising boats tend to sail shorthanded, with hands whose thoughts of fitness might centre around a gentle stroll to the pub.

In short, it makes a great deal of sense for cruising sailors to fit low-friction devices that will reduce the effort needed to sail their boats.

Most of this gear is assembled for life, with little or nothing in the way of disassembly being possible. However, there

are some dedicated products that can make life even easier still.

Notable amongst these are what are known as 'dry film lubricants', marketed under various brand names. These typically contain molybdenum disulphide and/or PTFE (polytetrafluoroethylene) either individually or in combination. They will tenaciously adhere to and lubricate many types of surface including:

- Metals.
- Plastics (phenolic laminates, Delrin®, Torlon® etc.).
- Natural and synthetic fabrics, including woven and laminated sailcloths.
- Ropes and cordage.
- And much else besides...

They aren't cheap but a little goes a long way. A quick squirt from an aerosol or a drop from a squeezy bottle will ensure that...

- Sliders – both on sails and sheet lead tracks – will slide easier.
- Ball and roller bearings (whether metal or plastic) will roll more freely.
- Your roller reefing headsail or main will ascend up its luff groove with more alacrity than ever before – very useful since both friction and weight increase as you haul it up.

Along with their lubricating properties, these products repel rather than attract dirt and also offer some protection against corrosion. All in all, not to be sniffed at.

JACKSTAYS

For offshore boats, a pair of jackstays to clip your harness on when going forward is almost obligatory – and with good reason. The horror of falling overboard, particularly in the dark, is not far from the fears of all sailors.

The usual arrangement is to run a jackstay down each side deck, attached to strong attachment points at either end. The options for the stays themselves is a straightforward choice: stainless steel 1 x 19 wire or polyester webbing, usually about 25mm (1in) wide. Although stronger and more resistant to wear, wire has rather fallen out of favour because it can roll underfoot, thereby presenting the ironic possibility that it might trigger the MOB situation it is intended to prevent. Webbing on the other hand lies flat on the deck and offers no such threat. At least not in that regard.

Unfortunately, polyester webbing doesn't have the durability of stainless steel wire. As we discussed way back in Chapter 2, polyester is susceptible to attack by sunlight – more specifically, the ultra-violet (UV) end of the spectrum. The same destructive process that damages our topsides will work its evil way with our webbing jackstays. If neglected they will suffer a considerable loss in strength over just a few short seasons, especially in sunny areas such as the Mediterranean. And you may never know by how much until it's too late.

However, if you treat them properly they will last for years. Here are a few pointers.

■ Choose a heavy webbing in the first place. 2000kg breaking strain (the same grade used for safety harness tethers) is often recommended, but safety harnesses don't spend long periods outside. 3000kg grade is a much safer choice. Not only is it stronger (obviously) but the heavier weave helps protect the inner fibres from the UV light.

■ Never leave the jackstays rigged when they're not required. It's amazing how many skippers do. And it makes no sense at all. At the end of each trip, take them in and stow them out of the sunlight. It only takes a few minutes and could save someone's life.

▲ **Polyester webbing jackstays are susceptible to UV damage. Stow them below when the boat isn't in service.**

CHAPTER 7

Hull interior structures

When you acquire a boat, whether new or second-hand, you can be forgiven for taking quite a lot for granted. Yes, you will surely form an opinion of its appearance, pleasing or otherwise, and whether or not its layout and other features suit your requirements, but when it comes to many of the structural issues, it's not unreasonable for you to trust the designer and builder.

For the most part your trust will be well-founded but there's no doubt that efforts to cut production costs have given rise to practices which, while helpful to the builder, can be a real pain to the owner when it comes down to repairs. Back in Chapter 6 we came across tapping plates and their associated problems but there are other issues.

DECK/HULL JOINTS

Many years ago the deck of a boat was found floating off Cape Hatteras, buoyed up by its foam-core construction. The hull – and the crew along with it – was never found. The conclusion was that the H-shaped aluminium extrusion and its associated rivets that clipped the two together had unzipped in heavy weather. Mercifully, such tragedies are extremely rare. But one can speculate that, of all the misfortunes the crew might have imagined might befall them, the parting of hull and deck was unlikely to have been one.

It used to be the case that deck hull joints were first bolted together and then glassed over internally so the hull and deck became one to all intents and purposes. Not often any longer. The modern practice is to use

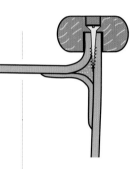

A popular method with older GRP boats. The hull and deck are glassed together internally but the timber toe-rail is very vulnerable to damage.

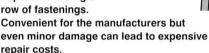

A typical modern system where the securement of the hull, deck and extruded toe-rail depend on a single row of fastenings. Convenient for the manufacturers but even minor damage can lead to expensive repair costs.

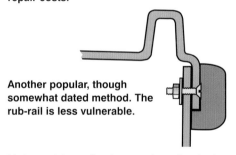

Another popular, though somewhat dated method. The rub-rail is less vulnerable.

high-modulus adhesives and mechanical fastenings – rivets on smaller boats, machine screws on larger. On sailboats, the usual practice is to include the toe-rail into the assembly as shown…

Structurally speaking, such arrangements are usually very secure, but problems can arise when damage occurs. A minor collision, say, might bend a stanchion and chew up a couple of feet of toe-rail, with the consequent repairs involving some major dismantling.

What to do

Depending upon who was at fault, it's time to let your or the other boat's insurers worry about it. Don't be deceived by the apparently trivial damage. Costs of repair can be astonishingly disproportionate.

INTERIOR CAUSES OF EXTERIOR PROBLEMS

Back in Chapter 3 we looked at stress crazing and discussed how 'hard spots' or 'stress raisers' caused by internal structure can abruptly restrict the natural flexure on the hull panels, causing them to fatigue and crack. Very often the first clue that anything is amiss will be found inside – perhaps in a locker or under the cabin sole.

There's no need to search deliberately for problems – just keep your eyes open as you go about your normal shipboard activities. Look out for places where the 'tabbing' – the GRP tapings that secure components such as bulkheads to the hull sides – has come loose or may have cracked through flexure. This is quite a common failing and isn't necessarily cause for alarm. But it should prompt you to inspect the hull externally at the next practicable opportunity.

Another possible stress raiser is caused by the acute corners made by bulkhead apertures and similar. These are often fashioned unthinkingly by builders, blind

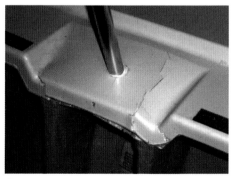

▲ Failure of an internal chainplate anchorage is the result of bad design. It's time to call in the manufacturer to put it right.

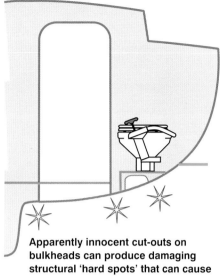

Apparently innocent cut-outs on bulkheads can produce damaging structural 'hard spots' that can cause serious structural damage.

to such little details, but they can lead to serious results. I once attended a 37ft motor cruiser with a slow leak that couldn't be traced. When in exasperation we craned her out we found one such corner had punched its way almost through the hull, splintering the laminate enough to allow water to seep through.

What to do

The exterior repair of stress crazing was covered in Chapter 3 but, as we read at that time, the damage will reoccur if we don't address the root of the problem – namely the existence of those stress raisers.

Here you should take expert advice, for the solutions vary with the specifics of the case. These might include:

■ *Bonding in short – preferably tapered – stringers between a bulkhead (or similar) and the hull side or ....*

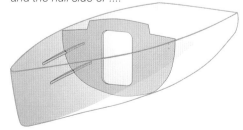

- *Introducing stress-spreading pads, possibly of plywood, where acute corners are doing the damage.*

Care has to be taken not to direct the stress simply to another location. The object of any remedial action is to dissipate the stresses so they can be absorbed by the structure as a whole.

GROUNDING DAMAGE

Unintentionally going aground can cause interior damage. Particularly susceptible are sailboats with high aspect ratio fin keels. Not only are they disadvantaged by their draught, but the keel attachments are spread over a relatively small area. Also the interior structure is designed primarily to support the keel's weight in a downward direction, not resist its upward thrust if you hit an inconsiderately placed rock at any speed.

As can be seen in Figure 7.1 the impact force will tend to punch the keel's trailing edge upwards. This can dislodge transverse 'floors' – the structural members that spread the load outwards in the hull – and even cause compression damage to internal furnishing. Following a grounding incident it's not unusual to discover that the hull and its stiffeners have calmly returned to normal while the interior furnishings – galley unit, heads, whatever – have been all but destroyed.

What to do

This is another case where it's impossible to be specific. Much depends on the severity of the impact. A minor nudge may result in no more than personal embarrassment, while a thunderous whack on something very solid may be cause for considerable concern.

If there's obvious damage, inform your insurers. They will probably appoint a

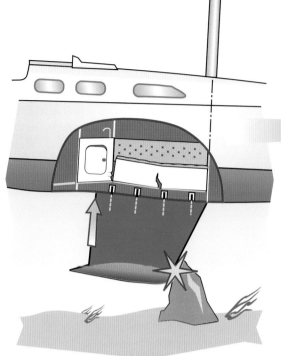

Figure 7.1: On fin-keeled boats collision with an underwater object can cause the after end of the keel to punch upwards.

surveyor to assess how extensive it is. In borderline cases, you may need to have it professionally checked out yourself.

Assuming repairs are deemed necessary you may expect the following:

- *The boat should be lifted off its keel to see if there's any distortion to the keelbolts. This will also allow external damage such as crazing or cracking to the hull shell to be repaired.*

- *Internal damage to the keel support structure is almost always best made good with the keel off. You can't glass over or around the heads of the keelbolts, for instance.*

- *Distorted keelbolts should be replaced with new. If the class of boat is still in production, replacements can usually be sourced from the manufacturer.*

And, talking of keels…

CHAPTER 8

Keels and their care

In the previous chapter we looked at the results of abnormal keel loads from the perspective of interior structure. Now it's time to look at the keels themselves.

At the risk of stating the obvious, their purpose is twofold. Their first job is to resist leeway, most importantly when beating. And here the yacht designer faces a dilemma. Keels are hydrofoils and the most efficient shapes are of 'high aspect ratio', meaning deep and narrow when viewed from the side. Unfortunately, along with that ideal come the twin disadvantages of inconveniently deep draught and structural vulnerability. As in most things, compromises are made.

Their second function is to provide ballast, thereby lowering the centre of gravity of the vessel as a whole. Within reason, the heavier the keel the more effective it will be; and it follows that the heavier the material, the easier that can be achieved.

Keel construction can be divided into three basic types:

- **Bolt-on keels:** By far the most common by virtue of their simplicity and

A simple iron keel will have its securing studs tapped into the keel itself with internal nuts to clamp the keel in place.

economy. Both single fin and twin keel configurations are found – the latter favoured mainly in the UK with little interest elsewhere. The keels themselves are most often of cast iron but can also be lead (actually an alloy of lead and antimony) on high performance and more expensive yachts.

The securing bolts or studs can be of stainless steel, galvanised mild steel or high-tensile steel. On cast-iron keels, the studs are usually threaded directly into the iron. This is impracticable with softer lead keels, so a bolt and gallery system is the usual choice, as shown below.

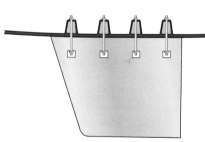

Since lead is too soft a metal to tap into, transverse galleries running through the keel allow securing nuts to be used.

Cheap and cheerful they might be, but bolt-ons have the potential to be troublesome. They can leak – though rarely seriously – and, as discussed in the preceding chapter, heavy groundings can cause interior damage.

- **Encapsulated keels:** Commonly found on long-keel traditional-type yachts or those with low aspect ratio fins. With these the foil profile is usually – but not

▲ Encapsulated keels are usually 'fit and forget'. Apart from internal corrosion problems, there's little to go wrong.

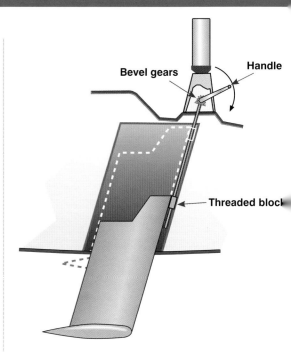

Figure 8.1: Daggerboard type keel mechanism.

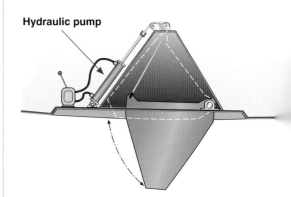

Figure 8.2: Swing type keel mechanism.

always – moulded integrally as part of the hull with the ballast fitted inside later.

As before, the ballast can be iron or lead, usually cast but sometimes poured in as a heavy slurry made up of shot in a resin binder. Combinations of the two processes are also practicable, with a shot slurry being poured in around a casting, thereby securing the casting firmly in place.

■ **Drop keels:** This type divides into two sub-categories. The first of these is the 'daggerboard' type where the keel slides up and down a more or less vertical slot (like a dagger in its sheath). See Figure 8.1. This is the simplest arrangement but has the disadvantage of intruding conspicuously into the accommodation – typically the saloon. Daggerboards tend to be fitted to smaller craft.

The second category is the pivoting keel type which swings up into an elongated slot. The Southerly range of yachts presents a good example of this arrangement. Though less intrusive, the engineering is usually more complex so it's more usual to find pivoting keels on larger yachts (Figure 8.2).

The keels can be very hefty, thus contributing the major proportion of the ballast, or may simply be flat plates, usually of steel, whose sole purpose is to resist leeway. Very often the weight will be divided between the keel and internal ballast, the latter often incorporated into the drop keel's mount.

Clearly the ability to reduce a boat's draught and creep into the shallows is hugely attractive but the mechanical complexity of even the simplest drop keels makes them the most troublesome of all types. Stones can become jammed in slots, preventing a keel from being lowered, and the complexity of their lifting system makes them prone to mechanical problems.

KEEL LIFTING MECHANISM

Let's start with the simplest:

- **Human muscle power** – Sometimes aided by some form of tackle (pronounced 'taykle' – the phrase 'block and tackle' is incorrect!) to give mechanical advantage. Although prone to grimacing, grunting and a propensity to complain, humans are fairly reliable if fed properly.

- **Mechanical winch.** This could either be a dedicated winch (sometimes a trailer type) operated from below, or a rope pennant can be led up to deck level where a sail control winch does the work. As above, tackles are often incorporated.

- **Electric winch.** As above but incorporating an electric motor.

- **Worm drive** – Where the lifting lug for the keel ascends up a threaded rod. The drive usually comes from an electric motor or by winding a handle manually on deck. Slow but reliable.

- **Hydraulics.** The first choice for larger boats. A hydraulic pump extends or withdraws a hydraulic ram that lifts and lowers the keel. There is usually a manual back up just in case.

Maintenance

All encapsulated keels can, of course, be regarded as part of the hull and will be treated accordingly. The need for any other kind of maintenance is limited to external and lifting keel types.

Assuming there is no sign of movement between the keel and the hull, the main preoccupation then becomes protecting them against corrosion – never a problem with lead keels, which are inherently immune. So let's concentrate on cast-iron keels.

- *Here opinions vary. There are those who advocate cleaning off any rust (often by grit blasting) then coating the keel with a proprietary epoxy system before antifouling in the normal way. My own view is that this is rarely successful and that a more conservative approach is both cheaper and more effective.*

- *Although nothing like as impervious to corrosion as lead, iron has good resistance and needs very little extra help. Surplus rust and any scaling should be removed (nothing like as fastidiously as for an epoxy treatment) before coating with several coats of a bituminous primer such as Primocon®. Then antifoul in the usual manner.*

- *The protection of steel, as commonly used for drop plates, is more challenging. To be frank, there's little you can do to keep rust away. Galvanising will help for a while but usually wears off as the blade abrades against its box. Again, Primocon® or similar will help but don't expect any treatment to be wholly successful.*

- *Maintaining lifting mechanisms will depend on the engineering specifics and, as usual, will be a mix of regular inspection and judicious lubrication. Hydraulic systems exist in a class on their own and some guidance is given in the next chapter – see page 55.*
  Drop board pivots lead a hard life and should be withdrawn every couple of years or so. Replace immediately if wear is excessive.

CHAPTER 9

Steering and other controls

Rudders are relatively simple devices but are amongst the most active mechanisms on any boat. They are, of course, moveable foils that use lift to direct the stern laterally from one side or another. With the exception of boats that use steerable drives, we rely on them utterly.

Rudders can be classified under a number of headings.

■ **Transom hung:** The simplest and often the sturdiest arrangement but also the least efficient because air can be drawn down the leading edge, causing 'ventilation'. At their very simplest such a rudder can be little more than a plank hinged along its leading edge on pintles (male) and gudgeons (female).

■ **Skeg hung:** These are mounted on 'skegs' – rigid fins protruding from the bottom of the hull. The skegs can be full depth or just partially so, a subject we shall visit anon. Skegs can be fitted to transom-hung rudders as well as those totally immersed. Type for type, this is the strongest arrangement, though only if properly engineered. Unfortunately, some skegs are too flexible to offer much in the way of extra support, so their structural contribution is illusory. However, the skegs do provide some directional stability – an asset particularly useful downwind.

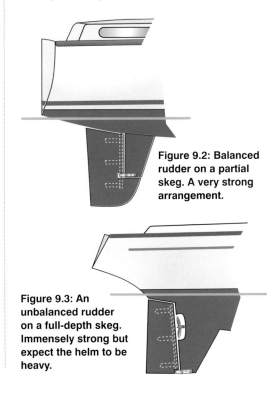

Figure 9.2: Balanced rudder on a partial skeg. A very strong arrangement.

Figure 9.3: An unbalanced rudder on a full-depth skeg. Immensely strong but expect the helm to be heavy.

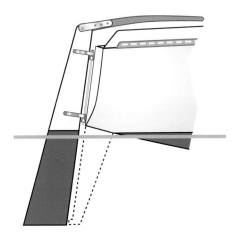

Figure 9.1: A transom-hung rudder may or may not have a skeg.

■ **Spade rudder:** These are invariably fully immersed and are 'cantilevered' – the structural consequences of which make them entirely reliant on their own strength. Although very hydro-dynamically efficient, they are also the most structurally vulnerable.

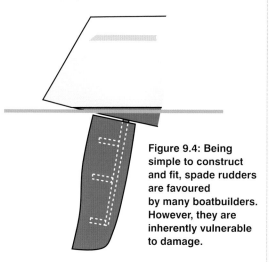

Figure 9.4: Being simple to construct and fit, spade rudders are favoured by many boatbuilders. However, they are inherently vulnerable to damage.

Rudders are also divided between 'unbalanced' and 'balanced' types. Unbalanced rudders have their whole blade area behind their pivotal axis, while balanced rudders – actually semi-balanced is a more accurate description – have part of the blade area forward of the axis. The latter produces a servo effect that reduces the loads on the helm.

Spade rudders and partial-skeg rudders are balanced, skeg hung are unbalanced, and transom-hung rudders can be either, though unbalanced is more common.

RUDDER CONSTRUCTION

The rudder blades on modern yachts are usually made up of two-part 'clam shell' mouldings bonded together with some sort of filler within the cavity. In repairing rudders over the years I've come across some rather eccentric fillers, including wood shavings, newspaper (in a Scandinavian language so I couldn't even read it) and even old rags. I hasten to add that this isn't the recommended approach. A better choice would have been closed cell foam, though even this tends to break down over time.

If the rudder has a stock, the most likely material is stainless steel but aluminium (importantly of the correct grade) and fibre reinforced plastic composites are also used. The construction of a typical rudder is shown in Figure 9.5.

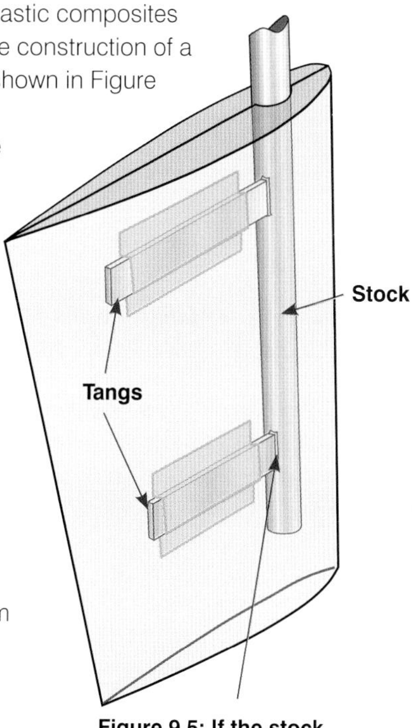

In the absence of accidental damage, the rudder assemblies themselves should need very little maintenance but there are a few points to watch.

■ It's almost impossible to prevent water from entering a hollow, moulded rudder blade. Even if the seam between the two mouldings is watertight, it will enter at the point where the stock emerges. On transom-hung rudders, the lower pintle/gudgeon unit and its fastenings is another likely entry route.

Stock

Tangs

Figure 9.5: If the stock turns and the blade doesn't, failure of the welds is the almost certain cause.

The good, if somewhat shocking, advice is simply to ignore it. Rudders have been known to weep for weeks after a boat is lifted out. There's absolutely no reason for the skipper to do likewise for there's nothing he can do about it. Adopting the principle 'if you can't beat them, join them' has prompted many owners to drill a small hole at the bottom of the blade, so the rudder can drain freely.

■ And neither should you despair if a GRP blade develops osmotic blistering. Immersed both inside and out, the laminate stands no chance in the long term. Again, be sanguine. It should continue to give satisfactory service for years with very little loss in strength.

RUDDER BEARINGS AND GLANDS

Whereas the rudder blade should need very little attention, the same can't be said of its glands and bearings. Although the rotational speeds are slow, the side loads can be awesome – particularly to the 'neck' bearing of spade rudders. Indeed, so overwhelming can be the friction that accompanies those loads that plain bearings become impracticable – the expensive alternative being roller bearings. These are water lubricated, requiring no maintenance other than periodic inspection.

However, on small to mid-size boats, plain bearings are sufficient. These are usually of plastic, with the clear winner here being Ultra High Molecular Weight Polyethylene – thoughtfully shortened to UHMWPE or sometimes even UHMW. This is a remarkable bearing material, being highly resistant to abrasion and water absorption (meaning it doesn't swell) and having an exceedingly low coefficient of friction. Less expensive acetals (Delrin® for example) can be used for less demanding applications.

Figure 9.6: Simple, reliable, with no chance of leakage, this arrangement is ideal on tiller-steered boats.

The simplest way of keeping the water out of the boat is to have the rudder tube rise to cockpit sole or even deck level – the obvious choice for tiller-steered boats. Figure 9.6 shows a typical arrangement.

This is less convenient for more complex steering controls which are usually hidden below. The design solution here is to lift the rudder tube well above the waterline, if possible, and fit a simple O-ring to keep any upward surge at bay (Figure 9.7).

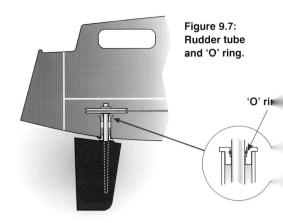

Figure 9.7: Rudder tube and 'O' ring.

'O' ri

If this is impracticable or the rudder tube ends close to or below the waterline, then a 'stuffing box'-type gland must be employed, similar to the ones used on propeller shafts (Figure 9.8).

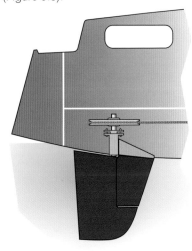

Figure 9.8: Stuffing box-type gland.

What to do

■ *Plain plastic bearings require no attention, but they should be inspected periodically for wear. At what point wear becomes a cause for concern is fairly subjective, so seek expert advice if you are unsure.*

If a bearing is seized onto the stock but rotating in the rudder tube then it definitely needs early attention, since the tube is suffering continuous wear that may be very expensive to rectify.

Upper bearings can develop irritating squeaks in dry weather, in which case they should be given a squirt of a PTFE or silicone-based thin film lubricant – but never a mineral lubricant that will remain sticky and attract grit.

■ *Stuffing box glands should be lubricated regularly – perhaps every month if in constant service. See page 110 for general advice on servicing this type.*

■ *Any O-rings should be replaced every few years, and certainly the opportunity should be seized to replace them if ever the rudder is dropped for any other reason.*

STEERING CONTROLS

This is a subject where technical variety is the norm. But at least we can draw reassurance from the fact that most types of steering mechanisms are appropriately reliable. However, failures do happen and prudent skippers will familiarise themselves with the engineering specifics of their boat and be watchful for any problems before anything too dramatic occurs.

A quick review of the alternatives might be helpful.

■ **Tiller:** By far the simplest, lightest, most reliable, economical and responsive system, but suitable for boat lengths only up to about 12m (40ft). A regrettable modern trend has been to fit wheel steering to smaller and smaller boats – a reaction, we are told, to popular demand. No one I know who has tiller steering would swap it for a wheel for any money.

That brings us to wheel steering, which comes in many forms.

▲ Connecting any form of self steering to a tiller is extremely simple.

■ **Chain and wire:** The most common type. The chain is similar to that on a bicycle and runs on a sprocket turned by the wheel. From each end of the chain run wire pennants (of 7 x 19 construction) that lead via turning blocks to a quadrant or radial wheel clamped to the stock (see Figure 9.10). Whichever is used, they should also be through-bolted or have a 'key' and keyway to prevent slippage. Although occupying more space than quadrants, radial wheels typically allow a simpler installation with fewer turning blocks. This is an important consideration, since the commonest fault is wear and fatigue to the wires where they pass over sheaves.

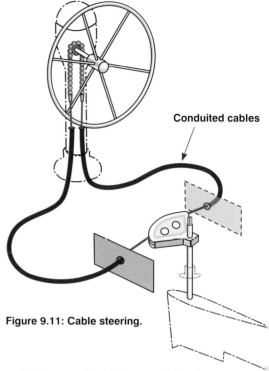

Conduited cables

Figure 9.11: Cable steering.

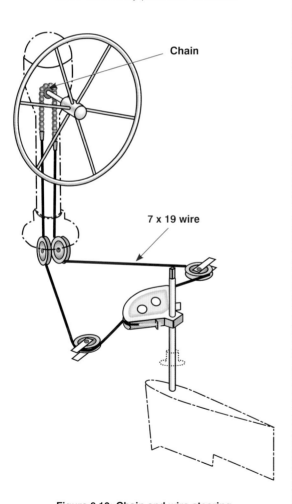

Chain

7 x 19 wire

Figure 9.10: Chain and wire steering.

■ **Cable steering:** This type divides into two categories: push-pull or twin conduited cables – also called 'pull-pull'. The push-pull variety has a single cable running inside an external sheath. It's often known as a 'bowden' cable, after its inventor Ernest Monnington Bowden, and was first used for controlling bicycle brakes. However, bowden cables are only capable of pulling while push-pull cables can perform both functions.

More similar to Bowden's principles are twin conduited cables – a pair of them being necessary as these can only pull (see Figure 9.11). The advantage of this type is that the cables can be withdrawn from their sheaths and replaced, while the push-pull type is sealed for life.

Push-pull cables are suitable only for light duty – a steerable outboard motor for example – while conduited cables will serve for much more demanding applications. The latter type is particularly useful in centre cockpit craft, since routing the flexible cables is relatively easy.

Maintenance: *Lubrication is the key to taking care of all these types, though the precise details will depend upon the specifics of each case.*

■ *Sheaves and gears need regular, but not excessive, oiling and greasing.*

■ *Wires should be inspected regularly and also benefit from being wiped with an oily rag. Look out for broken strands and replace immediately if you find even a single one. If one breaks the others aren't far behind.*

■ *Conduited wires can be withdrawn from their conduits for inspection and servicing. Take them out regularly (Edson recommend monthly) and lubricate with a PTFE-based (non-mineral) grease. Some installations have a greasing facility – a grease cup or nipple – built in, though it's difficult to see how injecting grease at just one point would serve the whole cable length. As before, any damaged wires should be replaced immediately.*

This leaves us with the last important steering category:

■ **Hydraulic steering:** Perhaps even more than conduited cables, the use of hydraulics allows helm positions – even multiple helm positions – to be situated virtually anywhere, since linking the controls to the rudder is via small bore pipes that can be routed wherever most convenient.

Basically, a hydraulic pump at each steering position pumps a specially formulated oil along the pipework to either extend or retract a ram. The ram acts upon a short tiller arm on the rudder stock.

A single helm position might use a system with no check valves – meaning that the interaction between pump and ram is a two-way one – i.e. the wheel can turn the rudder and vice versa. However, most systems – and certainly all multi-helm

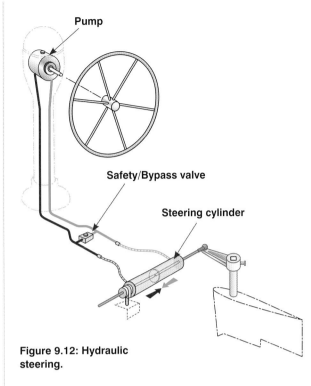

Pump

Safety/Bypass valve

Steering cylinder

Figure 9.12: Hydraulic steering.

installations, including autopilots – do need check valves. A typical installation is shown in Figure 9.12.

Hydraulic control systems are extremely robust, under even under the most appalling conditions – think earthmoving equipment! But they must be properly maintained.

Maintenance: *As always, awareness of developing problems is the first defence. Leaks are often visible but a fall in a hydraulic oil reservoir is a sure giveaway that fluid is escaping. Hydraulic systems are generally tolerant of very minor leakage but it should be borne in mind that leaks don't get better on their own, so early attention is by far the best policy.*

A feel of sponginess to the steering is an indication that air has entered the system. A good test is to put the wheel hard over and then release it. Air is compressible whereas hydraulic fluid isn't, so if the wheel bounces back you can be certain there is air in there somewhere. This means that you will have to bleed the system. Hopefully, the boat will have a manual describing the procedure. If not, the one that follows here is typical.

- *If the boat has a hydraulic autopilot, make sure it's disabled. You don't want it adding pressure while you work on the system.*

- *Find the highest point in the system – usually the uppermost helm pump but there could be a remote reservoir. Top it up.*

- *From here on you need two people – one at the helm and the other at the steering ram. While the first turns the wheel hard over one way and maintains a gentle pressure, the other person 'cracks open' (slacken, don't remove) the air-bleed screw on that side of the circuit – that's to say, the extended side of the ram. If bubbles emerge, continue bleeding until only oil seeps out. Then tighten the bleed screw and repeat the process with the wheel hard over the other way.*

- *That should have removed the air from the ram, so now it's time to turn your attention to the pipework. In theory, the bubbles should rise to the top of the system of their own accord, but the reality can be rather different. If all the pipework rises in a continuous slope there should be no problem, but this is often impossible to achieve when snaking through a boat's*

innards. Some sags in the pipe run are almost inevitable and trapped bubbles will have to be dislodged before they can rise.

- *If the system has a bypass valve – there to allow emergency steering – open it. If the installation has a single helm position, gently crack open the pump's fill screw. If there's more than one helm, start with the lowest but be very careful slackening off the screw because oil will flow down from above. A good trick is simply to gain enough slack so you can wiggle it between thumb and forefinger while being ready to 'nip' it up again.*

- *Next, spin the wheel first one way then the other. In twin-helm installations, turn one wheel one way and the other in the opposite direction. This will promote a circular flow through the pipes, hopefully carrying any bubbles along with it. You could also reinstate the banished autopilot to help in this tactic.*

- *Then, work your way through any remaining helm stations, working upwards towards the highest. Top up the oil to the recommended level and you're done.*

CAUTION: When leaving your boat for any length of time make sure the wheel is properly secured. Never leave it free to rotate.

SKIPPER'S TIP

EMERGENCY STEERING

All wheel-steered boats should have emergency steering. The usual arrangement is to have the top of the stock squared off so a tiller can be shipped. This isn't always easy to arrange when there's a steering pedestal in the cockpit so the tillers may need to be cranked to overcome the problem.

The wise skipper will ensure that all on board are familiar with both rigging and using the emergency steering.

TRIM TABS

Used only on motor craft, trim tabs are another device usually reliant on hydraulics. A typical trim tab is a hinged stainless steel plate attached to the lower edge of the transom. The angle of the plate is controlled by a hydraulic ram driven by an electro/hydraulic power unit inside the boat.

▲ A typical trim tab. Note the site where the sacrificial anode has been removed – correctly on the upper surface of the tab.

The principle behind trim tabs is simple. When the plate is angled downwards, the force of the water lifts the stern, thereby depressing the bow. Since the tabs are invariably fitted in pairs, variations in both trim and heel are possible. For example, if you lower the starboard tab, the port bow will drop and vice-versa.

Maintenance:

■ *Check the fluid levels in the power units. Most manufacturers recommend a minimum fluid level in the bottom of each reservoir with the tabs completely retracted.*

■ *Periodically inspect all electrical connections, both at the control panel end of the circuitry and at the power unit.*

■ *For saltwater usage, the tabs should be protected against galvanic corrosion with sacrificial anodes. The circular 'button' type is the usual choice and the anodes must be fitted to each tab's upper surface.*

BOW THRUSTERS

As average boat sizes increase, bow thrusters become more common. Smaller sizes are usually driven by electric motors. The electrical demands are high, so thrusters are usually supported by their own battery, situated nearby to keep the wiring runs short. If powered by the boat's domestic batteries, the wiring must be heavy enough to carry the current over the greater distance.

Thrusters are generally low-maintenance items. The drive legs are oil-filled but commonly sealed for life.

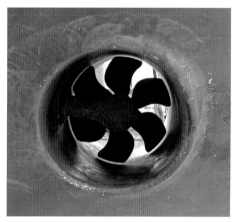

▲ Bow thrusters are extremely useful on boats with lots of windage.

Maintenance: Nearly all the attention they need is to the electrical system, since this is where malfunction or outright failure usually originates. This means:

■ *Battery levels and condition should be checked regularly. Low voltages will result in poor or no performance.*

■ *Considering the large currents needed to spin the impeller under load, it's absolutely essential that all terminals should be tight, clean and free from corrosion. This is true of all the circuitry but especially so for the main power leads.*

CHAPTER 10

Windows and hatches

▲ **On modern designs, windows have increased both in size and number.**

Although power boats had it rather better, anyone who was sailing around the middle of the last century would have been accustomed to spending their time below huddling in cramped and dark surroundings. Windows were tiny and hatches usually opaque – often of timber. Not much in the way of natural light made it below. It wasn't always much fun.

Nowadays things are somewhat different. By contrast, the typical modern yacht is well-lit and airy, flooded with natural light. This shift in trends has been driven by changes in both tradition and technology. Large windows were once considered a potential hazard – and with good reason, some would

still say – but that perceived hazard has since been reduced by the development of exceptionally strong transparent plastics and far superior sealants.

And there have been changes to the attachment methods as well. Whereas bolts or screws were once the only options, the windows on today's boats are often glued in place (see above) – a practice borrowed from the motor industry.

Boat windows can either be unframed or framed – with the first material of choice for frames being extruded aluminium.

So, what about the transparent bits? Well, again there are options:

Toughened (or tempered) glass:
Still a popular choice for framed windows since this is a very hard material, more resistant to abrasion and scratching than the other options. The toughening process involves cooling the glass in such a manner that its inner core contracts more than its surfaces. This puts the outer surfaces under a compressive stress that binds the whole together. Should the glass break, it's these stresses that make it shatter into tiny, relatively safe fragments rather than larger, more dangerous shards. Perhaps surprisingly, toughened glass can be flexed a little, meaning it can be sprung around small curvatures in the superstructure. More pronounced curves have to be pre-formed.

Unlike plastics, glass is impervious to damaging UV light so stands up well in the tropics.

Acrylic: Perspex® is perhaps the most recognisable trade name for this material in the UK. Much lighter and more shatterproof than glass, this material has been around since the 1930s and is far and away the most popular choice for boat windows – particularly for frameless windows because holes can easily be drilled to take the fastenings.

However, this is a relatively soft material, vulnerable to scratches and abrasion, and it's also susceptible to UV degradation over the years.

Polycarbonate: The fact that this is used for such functions as cashiers' windows and bulletproof vests is testimony to its immense toughness. The strength advantage over acrylic means thinner sheets can be used,

with consequent savings on weight – this, of course, is of great interest on high-performance craft.

However – and apart from its high cost – polycarbonate has one notable flaw. Exposed to UV light, its clarity gradually degrades, becoming foggy with time – if left long enough, even to the point where you can no longer see through it.

Maintenance:
■ *Glass windows can be washed as you might at home. Lots of soapy water and a soft sponge does the trick, perhaps finishing off with a chamois leather. There are a variety of spray-on water-repellent solutions that can help the spotting that comes with rain and spray, but in my experience the effects aren't long-lived.*

■ *Pretty much the same goes for plastic windows but, if using household products, make sure they are entirely abrasive free. Always use a very clean cloth – not one that's been languishing in a locker for some time. All it takes is a single particle of grit to put a scratch on softer materials.*

■ *Crazing to acrylic windows is simply a sign of old age – the scars of doing battle with the old enemy, UV light. Although the visual effects can be discouraging, the structural implications are seldom as threatening as they may look. Unfortunately, there's no panacea. Replacement is the only sure remedy.*

■ *Opt for low-phosphate cleaners/washing-up liquids as these have less impact on the marine environment.*

■ *Similarly, on unframed windows bolted directly to the hull or superstructure it's common to find small cracks radiating from around the fastening holes. As before, it's all a matter of degree and once again you must look towards replacement.*

Before we leave this subject, it's worth mentioning that to use countersunk fastenings is not best practice. The wedging action of the conically shaped head could have been part of the cause (see Figures 10.1, 10.2 and 10.3).

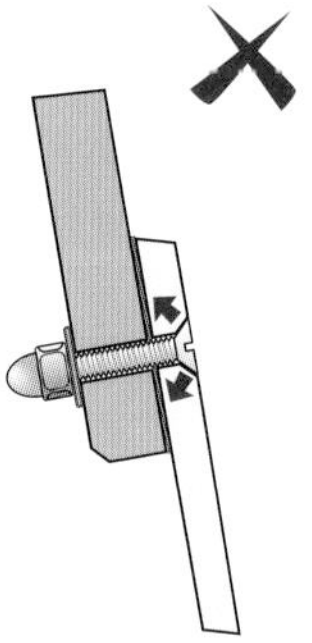

Figure 10.1: Countersunk fastenings should be avoided since the wedging action can cause localised cracking.

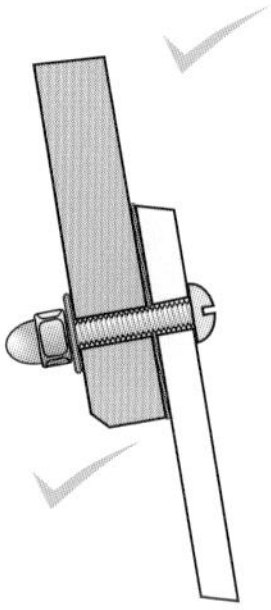

Figure 10.2: A better arrangement is to use dome-headed fastenings where there is no wedging action.

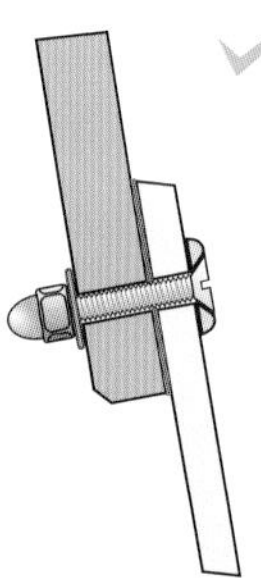

Figure 10.3: Better still is to use countersunk fastenings and cup washers which will spread the load to a wider area.

■ *Hardened sealant is another victim of weathering and old age. With time it tends to shrink and crack, very likely to lead to leaks. Slathering on external applications of silicone sealant might bring temporary relief but the writing is on the wall – it's time to fit new ones.*

HATCHES

The ubiquitous hinged acrylic hatch in its aluminium frame has almost entirely displaced those fashioned out of timber or GRP – and few would complain about that. Smart, efficient, and letting plenty of light in through their (almost invariably tinted) panels, they are just what we need on our boats.

Modern hatches are robust and undemanding to maintain.

Maintenance is pretty much the same as for windows – and that goes for the restore or replace issue. Most should give a couple of decades' service before they should be pensioned off. Beyond that they deserve being put out to grass.

SKIPPER'S TIP

NEW OR REFURBISH?

Whether to try and repair windows or replace them entirely is a question that has exercised many boat owners. I certainly know of those who have succeeded in extracting windows from their frames and then reassembling them in fresh sealant but it's a painstaking job.

I believe the general opinion is that it's hardly ever worth it. The cost of the raw materials – window and frame – is fairly low and they don't take a long time to make. All in all, replacement gets my vote every time.

CHAPTER 11

Spars and rigging

▲ Standing proud or about to fall? Masts are crucially reliant on the condition of the rigging.

The principle of 'out of sight, out of mind' is responsible for much of the mechanical neglect that can afflict a boat. But you can hardly say that of the mast and rigging, which is plainly visible for the most part. So, how about 'out of reach'? Many boat owners have only seen their mastheads from afar and have little idea what might be going on up there.

A modern cruising boat's spars are almost always of extruded aluminium – the ubiquitous 'tin stick'. Yes, superyachts and the flashier racers might go for carbon fibre but these are very much the minority. And aluminium is a good choice. Weight for weight it's an excellent engineering material, relatively inexpensive and inherently resistant to corrosion – the latter thanks

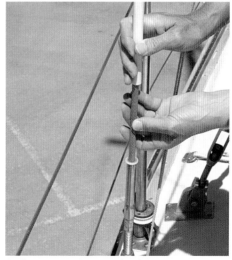

An important place to check is where the wire emerges from a swage.

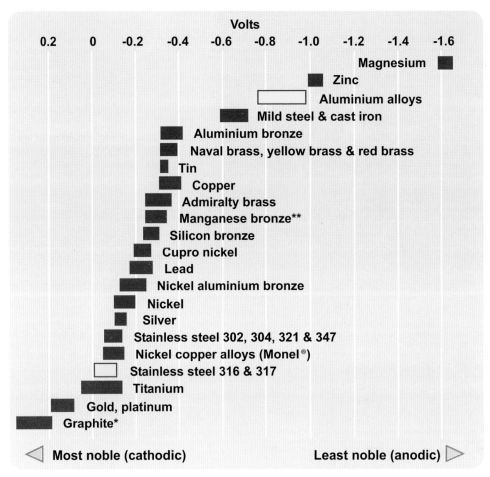

Figure 11.1: Galvanic series table. Note how far apart on the table are aluminium and stainless steel.

to a protective oxide layer that forms on exposed surfaces and 'self-heals' when scratched. This natural defence is enhanced by 'anodising' – an electrolytic process that thickens the oxide layer.

Unfortunately, in 'nobility' terms aluminium features low on the galvanic scale (see Figure 11.1) which means that it can suffer badly in the presence of other metals – including stainless steel, from which many of the mast fittings are made. Indeed, there's about 0.8V of potential difference between them. Galvanic corrosion is the cause of most of an aluminium spar's woes.

An advancement over the last few decades has seen the development of modular systems. The manufacture of

older spars involved quite a lot of welding whereas today's equivalent is made up of matched components that can be put together rather as one might assemble a kit. Speed, economy and adaptability have accrued – plus, of course, the ability to source spares should repairs become necessary.

This masthead fitting was found on a yacht about to set sail on a circumnavigation.

Crac

Maintenance:

Masts should be inspected at regular intervals. It is possible to do this from a bosun's chair hauled aloft (**Important!** See *How to Use a Bosun's Chair* in the Appendix on page 134) but this isn't ideal, since components like masthead sheaves will be at least partially concealed by the ropes reeved through them; and they could also be under load – not least the one serving the halyard used by whoever ascends.

Better by far to lower the mast, say every five years, so the whole length can be inspected on ground level.

Things to look for are:

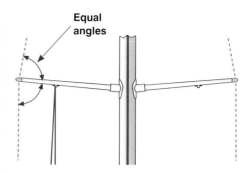

■ Corrosion between fittings and the mast. A common site is the heel casting that plugs the base of the mast. In advanced cases, swelling at this point can actually split the mast extrusion – clearly a serious source of concern. Where corrosion is severe, the fittings should be removed, then reattached applying a zinc chromate paste between the components to help quell any galvanic reaction. Split extrusions can sometimes be reinforced externally by riveting on formed plates. It's all a matter of degree.

■ Examine all shroud attachment points, looking for cracks to either the mast extrusion or the fitting itself. In this regard there is no such thing as a minor crack. All have to be taken seriously and professional advice should be sought.

Equal angles

■ Check the spreader mounts. It's very common to see drooping spreaders (often resulting from tension on flag halyards) so the mounts may be strained – particularly the socket type which is the most vulnerable. Look for cracked welds and loose rivets.

■ Make sure all sheaves are running smoothly and that there's no undue wear to their bearings. The photo below shows how badly these can suffer. Free or replace as necessary.

The original hole in this severely worn masthead sheave started life at only 10mm diameter!

■ Check for wear to the gooseneck assembly – something that can be done with the mast stepped. The use of relatively soft aluminium castings, rather than fabricated stainless steel, has made this an increasingly common problem.

■ Piston fittings at the ends of spinnaker poles should be worked regularly to prevent them seizing up. The occasional squirt of a PTFE lubricant also wouldn't go amiss, but don't use mineral oil which could smear itself over your precious sails.

STANDING RIGGING

Although such exotics as carbon fibre and stainless steel rod are used in rarefied forms of sailing, the standing rigging most are familiar with is made of stainless steel wire – more specifically 1 x 19 wire, so-called because it's made up of nineteen individual strands. The exception is adjustable backstay bridles, which are usually 7 x 19 wire to provide the necessary flexibility.

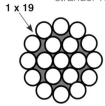
1 x 19

7 x 19

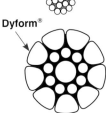
Dyform®

The terminals are either machine 'swaged' – meaning that once fitted they can't be removed – or of the hand-fitted type such as Sta-lok® and Norseman®, which can be disassembled and reused, provided they are in serviceable condition and you replace the internal cones. Although rarely found on boats falling into the 'modern' category, swaged eyes – commonly known as 'Talurit' swaging – are still found on older rigs. However, this type of swaging remains useful for things like davit hoists and tack pennants.

The prime enemy of rigging wire is flexural fatigue – also known as work hardening – and the more rigid the wire, the more prone to fatigue it is. It follows that 1 x 19 wire (or Dyform®) should never be allowed to flex much while 7 x 19 is considerably more tolerant. Since the security of an entire stayed rig is dependent on its stays and shrouds – almost invariably 1 x 19 – from henceforth we'll be referring to this type.

Misalignment and inadequate articulation lie at the heart of many rigging failures. Take a flexible wire – yes, even 1 x 19 is fairly flexible – and support its end so rigidly that it can't self-align, and the scene is set for stress concentration and work hardening. The quest for easier and cheaper fabrication has led some mast builders to adopt some methods which allow less articulation than older practices. This can be particularly true when there's a mismatch of products. For instance, one brand of stem-ball or T-terminal may fit awkwardly in a socket from another manufacturer, without the situation being obvious from the outside. We'll be returning to this anon.

TENSIONING DEVICES

Rigging screws, bottle screws, turnbuckles – the names vary from place to place – are terms that describe the same thing: screw-based tensioning devices used to tighten the standing rigging. Thankfully, this is an area where modern practices have definitely brought about improvements.

▲ Integral toggle.

Excepting the galvanised steel variety, older rigging screws were either entirely of bronze or stainless steel. Many remain in service to this day. The bronze ones of the breed were reliable but unsightly, their appearance not exactly enhancing the sleeker lines of modern boats.

On the other hand, the stainless steel ones looked great but came with one huge problem. If adjusted under load they had a tendency towards 'thread galling'. This is a phenomenon akin to friction welding that bonds interfacing parts together, making them immovable and, of course, destroying the rigging screw. This is a common phenomenon with metals that form a protective oxide layer – notably aluminium, titanium and, you have probably surmised, stainless steel. The friction wears away the oxide layer and, at a microscopic level, the matching surface profiles lock together.

The problem can't arise with dissimilar metals, which is why today's rigging screws typically comprise a chrome-plated bronze body with stainless steel threaded parts. For high-load applications this is an excellent combination and you should insist on nothing less.

TOGGLES

These modest little fittings are fitted below the rigging screws and add vital articulation at the point of attachment. There was a time when these were exclusively standalone items but it's more common these days to see them as an integrated extension of the rigging screw. All the same, a single toggle may not be enough – especially if there's some misalignment of the chain plate.

Maintenance: It should be part of your day-to-day routine to keep an eye on your rig from on deck but, as with the mast, the time will come when you want it all at ground level so you can give it a closer inspection.

Let's start with the sky-gazing.

■ *Look out for misalignment at either end of each shroud and stay. If this is very minor, there may be no immediate threat but at least it shows you where to look closer once the mast is taken down.*

■ *Check the mast for straightness – a rig tuning matter, nothing to do with the stick itself. The best way to do this is to peer up the mainsail track, where any deviations will be immediately apparent. (Advice on adjusting the standing rigging is in the Appendix on page 132.)*

■ *When viewed from the side, expect to see the mast bowed forward slightly. This is called 'pre-bend' and is intentional, helping the mainsail achieve an optimum shape.*

■ *It's not a bad idea to have the occasional look at the masthead through a pair of binoculars. Pick a calm day so you can hold them steady.*

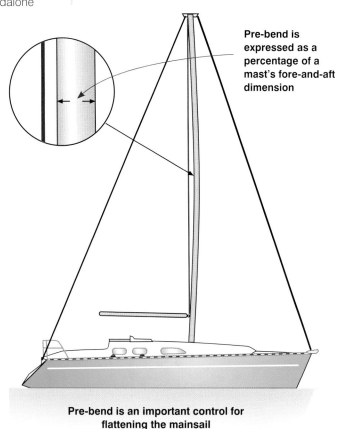

Pre-bend is expressed as a percentage of a mast's fore-and-aft dimension

Pre-bend is an important control for flattening the mainsail

By now you may have a stiff neck so let's conduct a more comfortable perusal of the rigging with the mast craned out conveniently horizontal.

■ *Look for broken strands – often to be found where the wire emerges from terminals. This takes more than a casual glance. As you can see from the photos below the problem may not be as obvious as you might think. Try flexing the wire to see if an end springs out. If a single strand breaks, don't be reassured that you still have eighteen strands left. The wire has fatigued and should be replaced.*

What you see...

... and what you actually have!

■ *Check for any longitudinal splits or cracks in the shank of roller swaged terminals. If any are found, the stay or shroud should be replaced.*

■ *Detach stem ball and 'T' terminals from their sockets and check for cracks immediately under their heads. Designs of both terminals and sockets have been improved over the years and a change to a more reliable arrangement should be considered. This is definitely a job for a professional rigger.*

The crack in this T terminal would be hard to see with the mast still standing.

THE TEN-YEAR RULE

The work-hardening process occurs invisibly, with no obvious warnings of impending disaster. The appearance of stainless steel wire changes hardly at all over the years.

An oft-quoted rule of thumb recommends that standing rigging be replaced every 10 years, though many believe this to be somewhat over-cautious. Much depends on the type of rig, how generously it was proportioned, and how hard the usage.

Boats with fractional swept spreader rigs are vulnerable, since the cap shrouds serve a dual purpose, resisting both the athwartship and forestay loads. Consequently, they are exceptionally heavily loaded. The actual backstay is usually of a light gauge, being there only to control mast bend. Another group rather more obviously at risk are racing yachts which, typically, are both lightly rigged and cruelly used.

If you are unsure what to do, take professional advice.

RUNNING RIGGING

This is another area which has seen significant changes with new, higher-performance materials emerging to serve the sailor. Let's take a look at what's currently of interest to us.

- **Nylon:** One of first synthetic fibres to take the stage; first formulated by DuPont as a substitute for silk and still popular today. Nylon is too stretchy for running rigging but is a very good choice for an anchor rode or mooring lines. It's quite absorbent and tends to stiffen with time.

- **Polyester:** This is the workhorse of the average sailing boat, serving all manner of applications – sheets and halyards being obvious examples. It has low stretch and is reasonably resistant to UV attack. The rope construction varies, but 'braid on braid' is the most common, meaning a braided core covered by a braided sheath.

- **HMPE (High Modulus Polyethylene):** Probably best known by the trade names Spectra® and Dyneema®, this material is one of the new boys on the block and is making inroads for certain applications. Stronger (weight for weight) and with much less stretch than polyester, HMPE is ideal for such roles as halyards and running backstays. It is often supplied as a hybrid with a braided polyester outer cover over an HMPE core. The cover adds no strength but protects the HMPE fibres and makes the rope easier to handle.

- **Wire:** Once favoured for halyards in 7 x 19 constructions, the use of stainless steel has been pretty much displaced by much more easily handled HMPE, but it is still to be found on some modern boats. Either a halyard can be entirely of wire (controlled by a captive reel winch) or is combined with a rope tail so conventional winches can be used.

Maintenance: Considering the abuse we heap upon them, it's astonishing that ropes are so enduring. To see a dozen years or so of service from a genoa sheet or halyard is not unusual – and even upwards of twenty years is not unknown. But it does help if we take reasonable care of them.

- *The two enemies are weathering and grime. We can do very little about the former but we're not so helpless about the latter. Left to their own devices ropes will absorb dirt, grit and salt, all of which are abrasive in their own way. These residues make ropes stiff to handle – irreversibly in the case of nylon.*

  Fortunately, polyester and HMPE ropes can be washed successfully. Either hank loosened coils to the guardwires or lay them out ashore and hose them down. Better still, allow them to soak in a mild detergent solution in some large container – perhaps the bath at home or even an inflatable dinghy filled with water.

- *Look for points of wear – rope clutches being a frequent culprit. And where possible, try not to let a clutch take a long-term load. For instance, after securing a halyard to its cleat, release the clutch to prevent its jaws pinching the rope.*

- *Rope life can sometimes be extended by turning them end-for-end, thereby moving worn areas to another less demanding location. Some skippers have eyes spliced at both ends of their halyards from new in anticipation of one day doing exactly that.*

CHAPTER 12

Sails talk

Whereas powerboat owners will find little of relevance in this chapter, sailing enthusiasts should certainly be interested. Sails are expensive. A good-quality mainsail for a mid-sized yacht can easily set you back several thousand pounds, which by any terms of reference is a painful hit to your wallet. In short, if you want them to remain serviceable, it pays to look after them.

The term 'serviceable' needs qualification. Some years ago, one of Britain's favourite boating magazines ran a series of articles where experts crewed on a range of readers' boats and advised them on how to get the best from their sails. In many cases the results were disappointing, not because the experts weren't expert enough but because the sails had deformed beyond the point of redemption. In some cases the readers were sceptical, suspecting the fault lay with the advisors. The truth is that there's a difference between a sail which appears physically sound and one still capable of performing with an acceptable level of efficiency. There comes a point where it becomes impossible to set a sail properly.

Chafe, stretch and UV attack are the foes. Sails are never better than when they are brand new, and it's depressing to learn that it's downhill from there. They start to stretch from the first time they are set, but the rate

There comes a point where sails are simply too old and stretched to set properly.

at which they do so depends on a number of factors. If your sails are built of too light a cloth, or have been carried in wind strengths outside their comfort zone, they can be ruined in a single incident. Then there's the sunlight. If they are left uncovered when not in use, their lives will inevitably be shortened.

Also, much depends on the quality of the sail and the material from which it has been made. The majority of sails are white and triangular and it's almost impossible to tell the good from the bad at a distance. Even close up it's pretty hard to tell.

It was once the case that new boats were delivered without sails, leaving it up to the owner to elect the sailmaker of his choice as he would go (as one did, of course) to his bespoke tailor. Elitist this might seem, but at least the responsibility rested with the owner. These days, sails are usually included as part of the package and it may be that the boatbuilder negotiated hard to obtain as keen a price as possible, with a consequent influence of quality. And herein could lie the problem. To expect long life from a budget product is to indulge in self-delusion. As in most things, you get what you pay for.

But, before we discuss how to take care of our sails, let's take a look at what's available.

Woven sails: The majority of modern sailcloths are woven from polyester fibres – chemically a close relation of resin found in our boats' mouldings. 'Dacron®' is a trade name that has become almost generic in the polyester sail context, having effectively displaced the British 'Terylene®'. Both are polyester products and identical in composition for practical purposes. Nowadays, cruising sails for the most demanding applications can also contain higher performance (meaning lower stretch) yarns such as Vektran® and Pentex®.

Sailcloths are amongst the most compactly woven cloths in existence, with their quality depending largely on the density of the weave. High-quality cloths are woven slowly and very tightly, while cheaper ones are woven on higher-speed looms that result in a looser weave. Nearly all woven sailcloths are post-treated by impregnating them with a plastic resin – typically melamine, sometimes along with other additives. This process helps stabilise

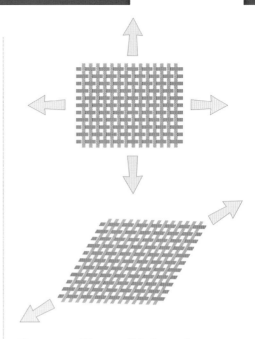

Figure 12.1: Woven sailcloths are less resistant to stress when loaded diagonally to the weave.

the cloth against distortion, particularly in the 'bias' – that's to say diagonal – axis (see Figure 12.1). The cheaper, looser sailcloths need more filler than the high-quality ones. Indeed, the latter are incapable of absorbing as much, due to their denser weave.

The proportion of filler in a sailcloth affects its service life. The flapping and shaking to which sails are naturally subject gradually breaks down the resin so the stability of the cloth diminishes over time. Overstretching the cloth can have the same effect in an instant.

Laminated sails: The last few decades have seen huge advances in this technology. Instead of the familiar woven cloth, thin sheets of polyester – trade name 'Mylar®' being representative – form a sandwich containing load-carrying filaments that can be oriented to match closely the stress patterns within the sail. Free from the over-and-under constraints of woven cloths, laminated sails can be precisely engineered.

The Mylar® itself has impressive structural properties, with the low-stretch filaments

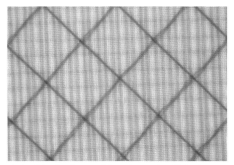

▲ **Is this the future? Laminated sailcloths are making significant inroads into the cruising market.**

– polyester, carbon fibre, HMPE, aramids amongst them – contributing yet more strength. Where weight is less critical, such as for cruising sails, laminates often have outer skins of woven polyester 'taffeta' to protect them against chafe. The relatively stretchy taffeta adds nothing to the strength.

The higher costs of laminated sails have deterred many non-racing skippers from buying them, but they are gradually making inroads into the cruising scene. Being quite stiff to handle, they are ideal for roller reefing systems where you simply wind them in or out.

And they do come with one big advantage. Whereas the deterioration of a woven sail can be represented by a straight line graph that declines from brand new to totally ruined, laminates degrade much slower in serviceability terms. This means the owner will see little fall-off in performance over the first few years, followed by a rapid plunge as and when the laminate breaks down.

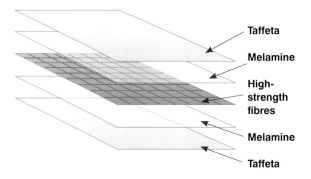

Taffeta

Melamine

High-strength fibres

Melamine

Taffeta

Care of sails

Let's deal with our three villains, chafe, stretch and UV attack, individually.

■ ***Chafe:*** *The bane of long-distance sailors, but a threat to all. A watchful eye is the main defence. Look out for areas of wear and have them repaired immediately. Particularly susceptible are points where a sail rubs against some other part of the boat – headsails rubbing against spreader ends or the pulpit, for example, or perhaps where a mainsail lies against an aft-led shroud. If the problem recurs regularly, consider having sacrificial wear patches fitted.*

Stitching is relatively fragile and always vulnerable. If you see it fraying, don't wait until the seam lets go, but take the sail to the sailmaker to have it overstitched.

■ ***Stretch:*** *Here, common sense and good seamanship are the main defence – though you can do little if the sail was too light in the first place. Reef early to reduce the total load in a sail and don't overdo halyard and foot tension – sometimes hard to resist if you're trying to flatten an already baggy sail. Halyards for roller reefed sails should be eased if a boat is left for any length of time.*

■ ***UV Attack:*** *Unavoidable when under sail, but it's astonishing how often you see sails simply bunched along a boom with no protection at all. Virtually all roller furled headsails have sacrificial strips so are self-protected when not in use.*

By contrast, mainsails – typically the most expensive sail on board – are all too often treated carelessly. Probably the best solution for cruising sailors is to fit one of the combined lazy-jacks and cover arrangements that cradle the sail when it's lowered. Even then, skippers often neglect to zip them closed or fit the hood that covers the sail's head, but there's no accounting for some.

Cleaning Sails

Soiled and stained sails certainly detract from a boat's appearance so the impulse to do something about it is understandable. But here you should be very cautious. High-quality woven sails will survive – even benefit from – being tumbled about inside a commercial washing machine, but not so your melamine-enriched budget sail that will be thrashed to within an inch of its life. A top-drawer sailmaker told me of the dilemma that sometimes faced him when a customer brought in a sail to be washed.

'Yes, we do launder our own sails, and also those from some other sailmakers but…'. And here he would tail off. 'Please believe me when I tell you that I wouldn't be doing you any favours if I bunged this… er… sail in the washing machine.'

So, what are the alternatives?

■ *Quite a lot of improvement can be gained by simply laying the sail out on a flat, non-gritty surface and giving it a light scrub with a mild soap (not detergent) and water solution. Some sailmakers recommend adding vinegar to the mix.*

■ *Use a soft-bristled brush to apply the solution before rinsing off with fresh water.*

■ *Oil and tar stains can be removed with a scrap of cloth dipped in petrol or lighter fluid but be careful (particularly in the case of tar) not to spread the stain further.*

■ *A very weak solution – no more than 3–5 per cent by volume – of domestic bleach will remove mildew, but its use is not without its risks. There have been reports that it can cause damage, chiefly to stitching. And NEVER use bleach on nylon spinnaker cloth or laminates.*

■ *If at all possible, dry the sails before re-bagging and stowing them.*

BATTENS AND BATTEN CARS

There's a downside to most things and that certainly goes for fully battened mainsails – most notably those with extravagant roaches as favoured by many multihulls. The battens' role is, of course, obvious. Without them the roach would collapse and the sail's aerodynamic properties would slump to nigh on useless.

Good-quality sails never use the sail itself as one side of the batten pocket. That's to say that the pocket is a separate envelope in itself and sew on to the sail in its entirety.

This is a sensible practice. The more roach there is, the greater the compression loads on the batten. And should a batten break or splinter – and you should believe that they do – their ends are invariably sharp and can do considerable damage to the surrounding fabric.

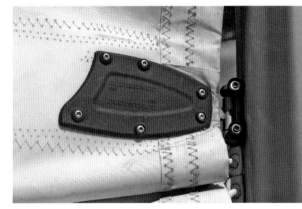

▲ **Full-length battens and their cars are becoming increasingly popular on cruising sailboats.**

Batten car types tend to vary with the size of the boat. The smallest craft can send full-length battens aloft on standard slides ascending the conventional sail track. Mid-sized boats do much the same thing but, instead of slides, they use roller cars that help reduce friction. The very largest yachts need a dedicated track and car system that's fitted to the after edge of the mast. The cars usually have 'recirculating' ball bearings to keep friction to the minimum.

▲ **Exaggerated roaches can impose significant compression loads on full-length battens.**

Maintenance: There isn't a lot you can do except keep an eye out for trouble. But here are some points to help you:

■ Look for wear points to the sail where battens might rest against standing rigging – a lower shroud or intermediate backstay, for example. Have sacrificial patches added if any are found.

■ Draw the battens periodically to make sure they are still intact.

■ Like all ball-bearing devices, the batten cars will benefit from the occasional rinse of fresh water to remove grime and salt crystals.

■ Keep a look out for worn roller bearings. Wear can flatten them to the point where the body of the car can scrape against the mast, damaging the anodising. Replacement is the only solution.

CHAPTER 13

Plumbing

BOAT WATER SYSTEMS – LIVING UNDER PRESSURE

Pressure water systems are another area where complexity has crept in to displace simplicity. Whereas a simple hand or foot pump once dispensed only cold water – subsequent heating involving a flame and a kettle – the pressure water system on a modern yacht or power boat now has hot and cold running water at the turn of a tap.

Whether a pressure water supply is a good thing or not depends on one's priorities and is, anyway, outside the scope of this book. But to be entirely reliant on an electrical device is to leave oneself vulnerable. The prudent boat owner would be wise to retain a manual system, if only as a back-up. To avoid the waste that inevitably goes with such a lavish supply, many ocean voyagers literally pull the fuses on their pressure water pumps while at sea.

Overall, boat water systems are pretty reliable. The only mechanically complex component is the pump, and long distance sailors can always carry a spare. A typical system is shown in Figure 13.1 and should be self-explanatory. But, just to run through the basics…

1 The fresh water is contained in a tank (or tanks) fitted with a stopcock to allow work to be done downstream should it be necessary.

2 On demand it then passes through a strainer which removes any debris that might damage the pump…

3 …which is the next stage in the water's progress. These are usually diaphragm type pumps with flow rates anywhere between 4 litres/minute to nearly 20 or so litres/minute, depending upon the water demand for a particular installation.

4 Immediately beyond the pump is an 'accumulator tank' – effectively a pressure buffer which smooths the water flow and prevents rapid on-off cycling of the pump.

5 Just beyond the accumulator the cold water supply branches off and goes to the various outlets – taps, showers, etc. – in the installation. An activated carbon

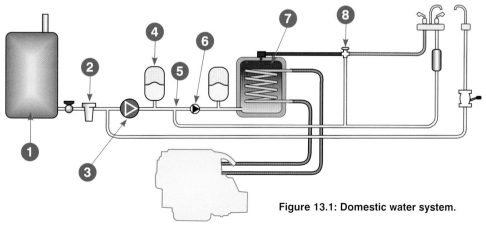

Figure 13.1: Domestic water system.

filter should be fitted to any outlets likely to supply drinking water.

6 Meanwhile, the pressure-driven water passes through a one-way valve and past an expansion tank. This is similar or identical to the accumulator but it does another job. As the name suggests, its task is to deal with the expansion in the calorifier as the water heats up. Without the expansion tank the pressure could build up sufficiently to open the calorifier's relief valve and water would be lost.

7 The calorifier is an insulated vessel containing a coil through which hot water from the engine is circulated. By simple conduction the heat is transferred to the surrounding fresh water. In addition, calorifiers often contain a mains voltage immersion element (not shown here) for use when alongside.

8 From the calorifier the hot – actually very hot – water passes to a mixer valve which combines it with cold water to reduce it to an acceptable temperature.

Maintenance:

■ *Most of the components are non-serviceable – that's to say if they fail they should be replaced.*

■ *However, the strainer should be inspected periodically and cleared if necessary. This will obviously entail closing off the water supply at the stopcock.*

■ *All activated carbon filter elements should be replaced at the beginning of every season. If left unused for any length of time, bacteria can build up inside them, with a possible threat to health.*

■ *Even if your shore supply is known to be potable, the occasional treatment with a water-purifying chemical is still advisable to inhibit any contamination in tanks or pipework. Sodium dichloroisocyanurate (mercifully abbreviated to NaDCC) is a commonly used substance but there are others. Always use in the recommended concentration.*

MANUAL OR FOOT OPERATED PUMPS

It would be remiss to leave this subject without mentioning these Cinderella objects of the marine plumbing world. Such is the faith in mechanisation that boats that come

A typical foot pump. Service kits are availa for most models.

with pressure systems fitted as standard rarely have a manual pump as a back-up. This, of course, leaves the crew hostage to the on-board electrics which – as most of us learn sooner or later – have a tendency to be fallible.

And there's a second reason to have a manual supply – water conservation, a subject of particular interest to cruising sailors. Frugality is much easier to control when you have to pump water by hand than it is when it's readily on tap.

So, what to do? The obvious recourse is to fit a manual supply to the galley which operates in parallel with the pressure one. If there's a spare outlet to the water tank (very unlikely) you can simply run a pipe from there, but it's more probable that you will have to tee into the pressure system pipework at some point. One might think that the most convenient location would be the cold water feed immediately below the galley sink but this won't do. Electrical fresh water pumps are demand activated – that's to say they sense the drop in pressure when a tap is opened. And unfortunately the arrangement of valves in a manual pump would be perceived as an open outlet by the electrical pump, which would spring into action and stay there until it had emptied the tank.

It may take a bit of burrowing but the place to tee into the fresh water pipe is between the strainer and the electric pump.

Maintenance: *Manual water pumps are simple devices that are easily serviced. Service kits – almost invariably complete with instructions – should be available for all current models and it's very advisable to carry one.*

WATER TANKS

Since one of the most precious commodities on any boat is drinking water, it follows that the containers used to store the stuff have to be of exceptional quality. Unfortunately, this isn't always the case.

A variety of materials are used to make tanks:

- Early tanks were often moulded in place, using the hull itself to form one of the sides. Although convenient from the construction point of view there are at least two serious problems. Firstly, that the water would soak into the GRP laminate, promoting osmotic blistering on the inside; and, secondly, that soluble compounds within the laminate would leach out to taint the drinking water. This technique is very rarely used today.

- **Galvanised steel** – a choice borrowed from the header tanks many of us have in our attics. Rust is a perennial problem.

- **Aluminium tanks** were also popular but suggestions that aluminium cooking utensils might be implicated in the development of Alzheimer's disease somewhat took the edge off their popularity. Whether this is true or not has yet to be established.

- **Stainless steel.** Still widely used and an excellent choice. Flexural failure or pin-hole corrosion to welds can be an issue, but these are generally reliable.

- **Welded food-quality polyethylene** – another worthy material. Because

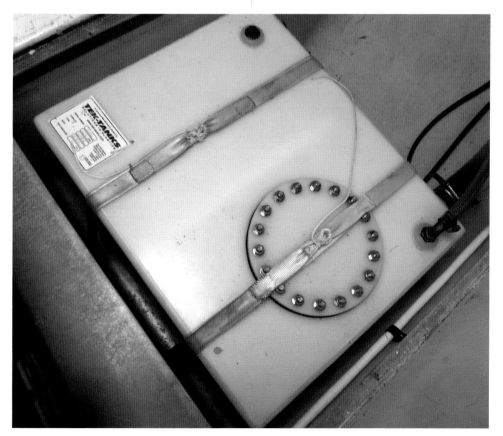

▲ Modern water tanks are often of welded polyethylene.

the material is fairly thick (10mm being common) the sides are exceptionally rigid and therefore resistant to the flexural fatigue problems you can have with stainless steel.

■ **Rotary moulded high-density polyethylene.** These are invariably standard off-the-shelf items, available in a number of shapes and capacities but not customisable like the previous types on our list. Compared to the others, they are economically priced.

■ **Flexible tanks.** These are available in standard sizes or made-to-measure. Being light and adaptable to awkward spaces, this is an attractive concept but they are susceptible to abrasion and subsequent leakage. On a delivery trip to the Mediterranean, a flexible tank burst. Fortunately, the boat was a catamaran with an identical tank in the other hull. Strength and durability depends greatly on quality. The best flexible tanks are double skinned, having a polyester reinforced outer skin and a food-grade polyurethane liner.

Manufacturers often adopt a fit-and-forget philosophy, meaning that tanks are often buried into unreachable spaces fit for nothing else. The irony is that most have access hatches so you can open them up and clean them. But that assumes that you can access the access hatch, which is far from always being the case.

Maintenance:

■ *If possible, open the tank and remove any obvious debris. With the tank dry, a vacuum cleaner is a useful tool.*

■ *Tanks should be sterilised periodically with a sterilising product (such as Milton®). The manufacturers' recommendations should be followed. In Milton's case this calls for 30 millilitres of solution for every 5 litres of water.*

ACTIVATED CARBON WATER FILTERS

There was a time when sailors lived with the vile flavours bestowed by plastic pipework – but no longer. To some extent we can ascribe these improvements to developments in the materials themselves – new food-grade plastics being less likely to leach chemicals into the water – but we also owe a debt to the latest filters. Carbon is one of the most absorbent materials around. When given a slight electro-positive charge – 'activated' in other words – it becomes even more so.

Impressive though they are, there are some points that should be understood:

■ Carbon filters do not sterilise the water, since they cannot remove bacteria or viruses. Because the water tastes OK doesn't mean it's fit to drink. Indeed, if left unused for any length of time, harmful organisms can proliferate in the filter. So…

■ Take no chances. Replace activated carbon filters at least at the start of the season – more often if the boat is hard used. Follow the manufacturer's advice.

TAKE CARE OF THOSE TOILETS

Excluding portable potties and primitive bucket-and-chuck-it devices, all marine toilets have a functional similarity about them. This is hardly astonishing since their purpose is a fairly narrow one – to receive and convey human waste to somewhere agreeably removed from a boat's accommodation.

It's in the 'somewhere removed' that systems vary. The options are:

■ The traditional method – and one still most commonly practised – is to pump the waste directly into the sea. It is only acceptable to pump out sewage into the sea at least 3 miles offshore, as the waste will be quickly diluted and dispersed by wave actions and currents. However, it should be mentioned that increasingly there are areas – often partially enclosed or non-tidal – where it's illegal and heavy fines can be imposed if you are caught. Figure 13.2 shows a typical direct discharge installation.

■ Another approach is to store the waste in a 'holding tank' until it can be pumped out ashore or discharged into waters

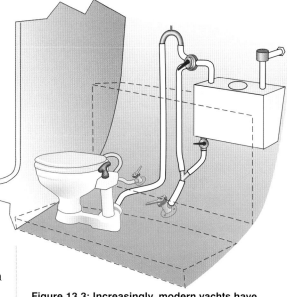

Figure 13.3: Increasingly, modern yachts have some form of holding tank fitted as standard.

where it will disperse and be unlikely to offend others. The installation shown in Figure 13.3 relies on gravity to empty the tank. An alternative which allows a tank to be installed in a lower position is to use a macerator pump. Find where your nearest pump-out facility is.

There are various types of on-board treatment, both chemical and electrical, that will sterilise the waste to a level where it can be safely discharged. Some use electricity to generate sodium hypochlorite (the basis of bleach) from seawater, others import chemicals from outside. Full details on servicing these units are laid down by the manufacturers.

For more general advice, read on:

Tips and maintenance:

■ *Not exactly a maintenance issue but it's important that proper sanitation-grade hoses are used. Lesser-grade hoses are much more permeable and will release unpleasant odours. You can identify the permeable type by wiping the hose with a rag dipped in hot water, allowing it to cool, and sniffing. If you get a whiff, you should consider changing the hose.*

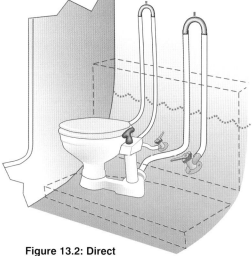

Figure 13.2: Direct discharge toilets are still to be found on older boats.

■ On a related subject, the stench that greets you after leaving your boat shut up for some time is from the inlet hose, not as you might expect from the discharge. When you closed the inlet seacock, the micro-organisms trapped inside the hose died and have since decomposed. The smell will soon disappear once you start using the toilet but some boats have an arrangement for filling the hose with fresh water before you leave it.

■ A common problem is the build-up of uric acid scaling inside the discharge hose. There are proprietary products to remove this although many skippers use white vinegar, half-a-litre of which should be poured into the bowl and then pumped slowly – meaning in stages so it can act on each part of the pipe – through the hose about once a month.

■ Toilets also benefit from lubrication – ideally by means of a specially formulated lubricant. For direct discharge toilets you can use vegetable or mineral oils, but not if you have a holding tank. The oil can float to the top, thus sealing the waste from the air, and promoting anaerobic decomposition and the odours that go with it.

■ Apply a light wipe of PTFE grease to the pump piston shaft. This will reduce wear on the seal so it will last longer.

■ Finally, carry a set of spare seals and valves for your toilet – along with instructions on how to service it. Marine toilets are relatively simple objects and can be stripped with basic tools. A pair of rubber gloves wouldn't go amiss either.

HOLDING TANKS

Yes, I know – another indelicate subject but one of necessary interest to boat owners who have to live with them. Unlike water tanks, the waste in a holding tank – particularly the urine – is quite aggressively corrosive. This limits the materials that should be used in their construction.

In this respect both stainless steel and aluminium make poor choices since both are susceptible to deterioration. This leaves plastics as the obvious alternatives.

Amongst those plastics is GRP. Freed of any consideration of imparting a nasty taste to their contents, moulded glassfibre tanks are definitely a practical approach.

But the clear leader in this field is polyethylene, either rotary moulded or custom-made out of welded panels. If anything, waste tanks should be stouter than water tanks – chiefly to prevent either the contents or their odours escaping.

Maintenance:

Hopefully nothing. A properly designed holding tank, appropriately ventilated to allow aerobic breakdown of the waste, should take care of itself without attention. However, there are ways you can help.

■ Specially formulated additives can be added. These contain enzymes to reinforce those already in the waste – the object being to stimulate the natural microbiological process.

■ Go easy on the toilet paper and avoid the luxuriously quilted types. Build-ups of paper are perhaps the commonest cause of blockages. A useful boat rule that concentrates the mind wonderfully is: 'You block it, you clear it!'

■ And NEVER put other objects into a marine toilet. The head's pump might let them through but a macerator could choke on them. And, even if there is no macerator, they can settle to the bottom of a tank and accumulate, again possibly causing blockages. The old saying that you should never put anything in the bowl that hasn't been eaten first has a lot going for it.

CHAPTER 14

Cooking afloat

COPING WITH COOKERS

A well-fed crew is a happy crew goes the saying, and there's no disputing that the facilities for satisfying even the hungriest of shipmates has improved vastly over the years. Indeed, the modern galley can easily be as well-equipped and as sumptuous as a kitchen ashore.

Gone are the days of smoky, sputtering and exasperatingly neurotic paraffin stoves. Today's cookers are much more user-friendly.

They fall into three fuel types:

1. Methylated spirits (alcohol)

This is a relatively inefficient fuel that releases less heat than the other commonly used fuels. It's usually only found on daysailers and power boats – often combined with an AC powered ring for use when alongside. Pressurised alcohol cookers are somewhat more efficient but are not popular – possibly because methylated spirits isn't cheap.

2. Diesel

The attractions of carrying a single-type fuel for all purposes certainly has its attractions and there are some excellent diesel cookers around. However, there are installation requirements which are awkward to say the least. Diesel stoves need chimneys to convey toxic combustion gases beyond the confines of the boat. Simple ventilation is not enough. Although some flexibility is possible, this cumbersome arrangement makes gimballing difficult.

Diesel cookers need an electric fan to assist the combustion process.

3. Liquefied Petroleum Gas

This is far and away the most popular fuel, and is often described by the acronym LPG. The word 'liquefied' gives a clue as to how it is stored.

LPG as we know it is a cocktail of light hydrocarbons that are gaseous at most normal temperatures but becomes liquid under pressure. The two principal ingredients are butane and propane, with butane being the easiest to store as a liquid, requiring a pressure of only about 2 bar. Those inexpensive plastic cigarette lighters we toss about so casually contain butane – a measure of how easily it can be contained. By contrast, propane must be stored at around 7 bar but rewards the extra effort by turning into a gas at lower temperatures. This makes it more suitable for colder climates.

Many of the commercial gases we buy are usually a mix of the two, with the proportions adjusted to suit local conditions. However, they may be labelled 'propane' or 'butane' depending on which is the primary gas and which, if any, is the additive. In the UK propane is usually delivered in red cylinders, butane in blue.

In gaseous form, both butane and propane are heavier than air. This means that any leakage will tend to sink towards the bilges where, mixed with oxygen in certain concentrations, it can become a serious explosive threat. This makes some sailors very wary of using LPG as a fuel, though it has to be said that, provided the installation is properly designed and maintained, the overall safety record is good.

GAS SAFETY

The precautions

The specifics of how a gas installation should be designed is something of a grey area, with conflicting opinions prevailing in certain countries. Some take the view that the fewer joints there are in the supply line, the lesser the risks of leakage and, therefore, the safer the installation. This might allow the use of flexible hose throughout so long as it is of approved type, visible along its entire length, and regularly replaced – every 5 years being a typical maximum.

The British attitude, on the other hand, prefers the main run of the supply to be in seamless copper or stainless steel pipes with short (no more than 1m) lengths of flexible hose at the cylinder end and also at the cooker (if gimballed). This is a logical solution when pipework is routed behind cabin structure and can neither be inspected nor replaced.

Rather than explore all the options, for our purposes let's stick with the well-regarded CORGI recommendations we're familiar with in the UK.

Figure 14.1 shows a typical installation.

A The cylinder(s) are stowed in a locker, sealed from the boat's interior but vented to the open air. The vent must be high enough above the waterline so it remains clear when the boat heels.

B The regulator and shut-off valve can be mounted directly onto the cylinder or close nearby inside the locker.

C A bubble tester is not an absolute requirement but is strongly recommended. It contains a liquid which can be viewed through a small glass window. Any bubbles in the liquid are an indication of leakage downstream.

D A seamless copper or stainless steel pipe conveys the LPG to the vicinity of the appliance, using grommets where it passes through bulkheads and clips to give it intermediate support.

E The pipe terminates at another stop-cock, located near the appliance (our cooker) but not in a position where it couldn't be closed in the event of a galley fire. In other words you shouldn't have to reach over the cooker to turn off the gas.

F The final link in the supply route is via an armoured flexible hose which allows the cooker to swing on its gimbals. Note that the armouring is only there to prevent pinching damage. Under the armouring is an ordinary gas hose that must be replaced as often as all the others.

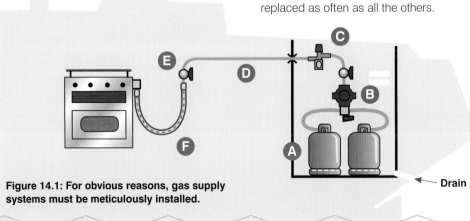

Figure 14.1: For obvious reasons, gas supply systems must be meticulously installed.

Drain

COOKERS

LPG cookers are relatively simple devices that have developed only slowly over the years. The most important of these are the flame-failure devices(FFDs) which switch off the gas at the burner if the flame blows out.

The device that performs this trick is called a thermocouple. It consists of a sensor made up of two different metals lying in contact with each other. When the sensor is heated, a small electric current is created. This energises an electromagnet inside the fuel supply valve that latches it in the 'open' position, thus allowing the flame to remain alight. Such valves are spring-loaded and must be held in manually, giving a few seconds for the sensor to heat up.

FFDs cannot be serviced. If defective, they must be replaced.

▲ **The safety of LPG cookers and their supply depends on good installation standards and ongoing vigilance.**

CAUTION

The Recreational Craft Directive (RCD) sets out to establish common design and constructional standards across Europe for every vessel (over 2.5m and with some other exceptions) built or imported into the region. It became mandatory on the 16th of June 2003.

One of its demands is that every burner on any LPG appliance be fitted with a flame failure device. But this only applies to new vessels. There is no obligation to upgrade older ones.

The upshot of this is that there are many boats still in service installed with gas appliances that would now be considered unsafe. The oldest cookers could have no FFDs at all while others might have them fitted only to the grill and oven burners.

So, the message to anyone buying an older boat is that they should identify what they're getting and seriously consider whether or not an upgrade is appropriate.

CHAPTER 15

Dealing with diesels

Diesel engines are tough. They have to be. That well-used description of how they work – suck, squeeze, bang and blow – hints at the brutal world they live in. To understand it better, let's take a quick look at that sequence:

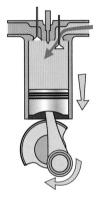 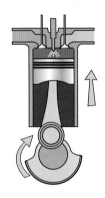 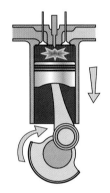 

Suck: first a fuel and air mix is sprayed into a cylinder.

Squeeze: the piston rises, compressing the mixture until it becomes hot enough to…

Bang!…explode, driving the piston to the bottom of its stroke.

Blow: the exhaust gases are purged from the cylinder ready to start the cycle again.

The forces involved are prodigious – far greater than in an equivalent petrol engine which relies on a spark to ignite the fuel. Bearings come under immense loads, placing exacting demands both on the engineering and the lubricants that make everything turn smoothly. Tough they might be but they don't like being neglected. Take care of your engine and it will take care of you.

When it comes to maintaining boat engines, the task can be as simple or as complicated as we care to make it. As a skipper, your relationship with that oil-filled lump lurking in the shadows could be as detached as having total reliance on the nearest engineer; or it could be as involved as digging out your tools and conducting a strip-down and rebuild.

I suspect that most of us would be satisfied with falling somewhere between those two extremes – perhaps willing to offer a bit of day-to-day care but reluctant to take on major surgery.

But what sort of care are we referring to? What exactly does it entail and how frequently should we fulfil those tasks that will be involved?

Well, there are some pacing influences. In most parts of the world, boating is a seasonal pursuit, with alternating periods of activity and dormancy. These ebbs and flows make some times more convenient than others. There are also physical limitations to the useful lifespan of many of the substances and components – lubricating oils become contaminated, filters clog, anodes waste away, and so on. It therefore makes sense to try and match what's opportune for us with what's good for the engine.

What we need is a schedule.

BASIC MAINTENANCE INTERVALS

Daily when in use

- *Check fuel level.*

- *Check crankcase oil level.*

- *Check fresh water coolant level. Remember that it's extremely dangerous to open the header tank while it's still hot.*

- *Conduct a general check for leakage of oil, fuel or water.*

Weekly when in use

- *Check belt tensions and inspect for damage. See page 101.*

- *Check gearbox oil level.*

- *Check for water or sediment in the fuel tank. Inspect the pre-filter bowl or drain off a sample from the bottom of the tank.*

- *Check raw water strainer and clear if necessary.*

- *Check battery electrolyte levels. Top up if low.*

Annually

- *Check cooling system anodes, replacing as necessary.*

- *Closely inspect all hoses for cracking, bulging or other signs of deterioration. Check all hose clips for tightness.*

- *Check the air filter, wash or replace as appropriate.*

- *Check the exhaust elbow for corrosion. Ideally, you should detach the exhaust so you can have a look inside.*

Exhaust elbows are a common source of trouble. Here a weld has failed, dripping water onto the electrics below.

- *Check engine mounts for deterioration. Look for loose fastenings and separation between rubber and metal components.*

- *Check the shaft coupling and make sure all bolts are properly tightened.*

As recommended by the engine manufacturer

Certain jobs relate to engine hours and can arise at any time, depending on how much the boat is used. You should refer to your engine manual for the precise details but the following are typical.

- *Oil and oil filters should be changed every 100 to 150 operational hours or at the end of each season, whichever comes first.*

- *Gearbox oil (or transmission fluid) should also be changed every 150 hours or annually, whichever comes first.*

- *Replace fuel filters every 300 hours.*

- *Saildrive diaphragms should be replaced after 7 years.*

SCHEDULED BY THE SEASONS

The reality is that most of us shuffle our maintenance plans to fit the calendar, and there's usually no reason why not. The average sailing yacht will spend only about 50 hours per year under power and even a motor cruiser would be pushed to make 150.

The all-important oil changes can therefore be scheduled as an annual event, and the time to start is when your boat is being put to bed for the winter. That way, the acids that are produced as a by-product of combustion won't be left to eat away at metal surfaces over the lay-up period. The other advantage of giving the engine a good going over in the autumn is that it leaves you plenty of time to rectify any problems you discover.

Some boats are laid up ashore while others remain afloat. It follows that jobs that might be possible in one situation won't be in the other. Do what you can.

WINTERISING

- Change the engine and gearbox lubrication oil, replacing any filters. It is better to do this before the lay-up rather than leave it until the spring. This removes the acids that have accumulated in the old oil. Oily rags and oil filters should be disposed of as hazardous waste, either at the marina or at your local household waste recycling centre.

- Drain the fresh water cooling system and refill with a fresh solution of antifreeze.

- Flush the raw water system through with fresh water if possible.

- Check the raw water filter. Clean if necessary.

- Remove the pump impeller. Pop it into a plastic bag and tie it to the keys so you won't forget to refit it!

- Drain any water or sediment from the fuel tank and fill the tank if possible.

- Also drain any contaminants from the pre-filter. Replace the filter element.

- If possible, squirt a little oil into the air intake and turn over the engine (don't start it!) to distribute it over the cylinder walls. Some manufacturers recommend removing the injectors and introducing the oil that way – refitting the injectors once you have done so.

- Change the air filter and stuff an oily rag into the intake. Do the same to the exhaust. Then hang a notice on the engine to remind you they are there!

- Relax or remove all belts. If the former, relax them enough to be obvious.

- Rinse out the anti-siphon valve with fresh water. Reassemble if you've taken it apart.

- Check the engine over thoroughly. Your inspection should include: the engine mounts, hoses and their clamps, exhaust and the exhaust elbow, and the electrical wiring. If there's something amiss, this is the time to know about it.

- Remove the batteries and charge them fully. If the boat is to be wintered afloat, clean the terminals and protect them with petroleum jelly. Wherever they are, recharge them every month or so.

ONCE SPRING HAS SPRUNG

- Check oil levels and top up if necessary.

- Check fresh water coolant and top up if necessary.

- Refit pump impeller.

- Unseal any openings you might have plugged in the autumn.

- Re-tighten all belts.

- Reconnect batteries.

- Check stern gland lubrication. Give the remote greaser a couple of turns.

- Start the engine.

- Enjoy!

A TYPICAL DIESEL FUEL SYSTEM. TAKE THE TOUR

What is diesel fuel?

Diesel fuel is basically a distillate of crude oil, to which various other ingredients are added. Producers often vary the precise composition to suit local and seasonal conditions. Although the brand name on the pump might be the same, a fuel sold in the tropics will not be identical to one formulated for cold climates. You may encounter starting problems when moving from one region to another, though relatively modest climatic changes will probably go unnoticed.

The basic system

A typical fuel system forms a circuit, around which the fuel passes in an endless parade. It starts from the tank where the fuel is stored and is then drawn through a pre-filter by the lift pump. From there it goes through yet another (finer) filter before reaching the injection pump. This helps itself to however much the engine wants and sends it on to each of the injectors in turn. The surplus fuel

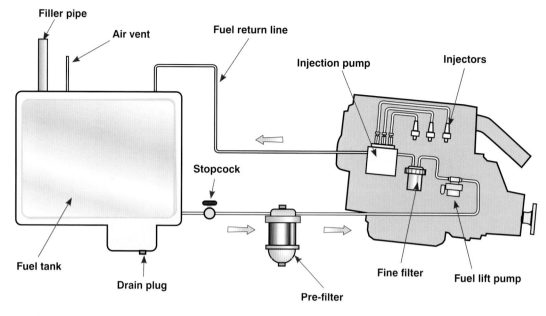

Figure 15.1: Basic diesel system.

goes back to the tank, via the return pipe, to join the queue again. The lift pump, fine filter, injection pump and injectors are all parts of the engine. The tank, shut-off cock, pre-filter and most of the fuel lines are supplied and fitted by the boat builder or engineer. Let's look at them one at a time.

MORE TROUBLES WITH TANKS

As with the water and holding tanks already covered in previous chapters, this is one of those fit-and-forget items few of us even bother to think about – yet it's here that many of our troubles begin. Diesel tanks can be made from a wide variety of materials: mild steel, stainless steel, aluminium, GRP, moulded or welded polyethylene, or nitrile rubber-impregnated fabrics – the last, of course, being flexible.

Perhaps the most potentially treacherous is mild steel. A tank might appear sound from the outside but could be severely rusted within. The rust is caused by water condensation and there's some debate as to how this arises. Many argue that it's simply due to the temperature changes that occur between day and night. As the fuel

level drops, moist air is pulled in through the vent. A minority opinion claims that there can never be enough water vapour inside a tank – not even a nearly empty one – to have a significant effect. This last group would point the accusing finger towards water contaminated fuel – either tainted at source or later through the air vent or a leaking filler cap.

All of this makes for fascinating discussion but is of little consolation to the boat owner. The fact is that mild steel tanks can and do rust internally, and the detritus thus formed can very quickly block the pre-filter. But rust isn't the only threat.

The diesel 'bugs'

Microbiological contamination of the fuel can pose a serious problem. A variety of organisms – including bacteria, yeasts, fungi and algae – can thrive in the mix of water and fuel that lies at the bottom of many tanks. The organisms arrive either in contaminated fuel, or as airborne spores, entering through vents and filler hoses. As they grow, die and biodegrade the fuel, they form a slimy black, brown or green sludge that can quickly plug the filters and bring the whole system to a standstill. The sludge is very corrosive, capable of doing serious damage to components it contacts.

This is a major headache. Biocides will kill the little varmints, but their corpses remain unless physically removed. Since they need both fuel and water to survive, the best protection is to make sure there's little or no moisture in the tank. Some experts recommend routinely dosing the fuel with a biocidal additive as a preventative measure. Others believe you should wait until action is needed.

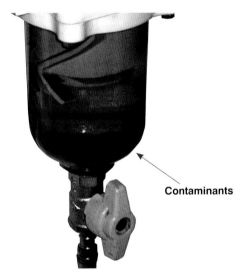

Despite the presence of contaminants in this pre-filter it continued to function normally.

BACK TO TANKS

Most of us live with the tanks the boat builder supplied. The only time we're offered a choice in the matter follows the failure of the original – a minor disaster as the mess can be appalling. However, it can provide a welcome opportunity to improve the installation.

We've already touched briefly on the choice of materials – the vices and virtues of which they share with other types of tank. But, in their design, fuel tanks have some notably special features.

Although it isn't always possible to

arrange, ideally all fuel tanks should have a drainage sump at their lowest point. Since water is heavier than diesel fuel, it will sink to the bottom and collect in the sump (Figure 15.2). It should then be a relatively simple task to open a drain cock and draw off any water lying there.

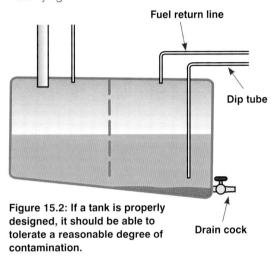

Figure 15.2: If a tank is properly designed, it should be able to tolerate a reasonable degree of contamination.

An alternative is to have the outlet some distance above the tank's base or a dip tube-type outlet (see Figure 15.2). By drawing the fuel from a few centimetres above the bottom of the tank, you minimise the risk of including water and heavy sediment with it. Of course, this means that you effectively reduce your tank's capacity, but it's never sensible to run the dregs through your system anyway.

A third option is to have an accessible inspection hatch, through which a hand pump (of the Pela type, see page 98) can be inserted. Either way, as soon as pure, clean diesel fuel starts to emerge, you will know you have removed a significant threat. And look out for sediment which might warn of the existence of bugs. A sample from the depths will tell you a lot about the health of your fuel system.

So, let's follow the fuel's progress from there.

WATER SEPARATING FILTER (PRE-FILTER)

The first defence against contaminated fuel is to be careful where you buy it. The second is your pre-filter, most types of which will also strip water from the fuel.

A typical example is shown in Figure 15.3. The fuel enters through the inlet 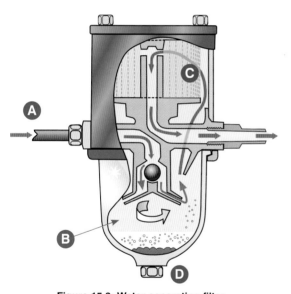**A** and is sent downwards into a bowl **B**. There, an arrangement of fixed vanes causes the fuel to rotate, creating a centrifugal effect that separates water particles and heavy sediment and deposits them in the bottom of the bowl. The fuel then rises inside the casing and passes through a filter element **C** before being sent on to the engine.

Figure 15.3: Water-separating filter.

The bowl may either be of glass or metal or plastic. Transparent bowls allow you to see if any contaminants have been collected, in which case they can be drained off through the valve or plug **D**. Opaque bowls need draining periodically, just in case. Some filters have a pair of electrodes that, when immersed in collected water, will complete an electrical connection to sound a warning alarm.

FUEL LIFT PUMP

The role of these relatively simple devices is to deliver fuel to the injector pump. Actually, they deliver an excess of fuel. Injector pumps will take only a little of what's on offer, using what remains to lubricate and cool their mechanisms before sending it back along the return pipe to the tank (see Figure 15.1). Since the amount they deliver isn't critical, lift pumps can afford to keep plenty in hand to offset unhelpful influences – such as resistance caused by partially clogged filters or the suction head arising from tanks mounted low.

The most common type of lift pump is driven directly by the engine, and often has a small external handle so it can be operated manually for bleeding air from the system. Although there was a time when they could be stripped and serviced, modern ones are often throw-away units supplied complete. However, there's no cause for concern here. Lift pumps are both reliable and long-lived. It's not unusual for them to complete thousands of hours of service.

FINE FILTER

In cleanliness terms this is the last gateway. Beyond this point the fuel goes on to the most expensive single item of kit on the whole engine – the injection pump – where even the tiniest particle of grit can cause grievous damage.

Filters are categorised by the size of the particles they allow through. The customary unit used to define particle size is the micron – one millionth of a metre. And, whereas a typical pre-filter might fall into the 10–50 microns range, the fine filter is more stringent at 2–10 microns.

At this point we should sing a short paean of praise in favour of two-stage filter systems. Diesel fuels contain tarry particles called 'asphaltenes'. Being small, soft and pliant, they present no serious threat to the fuel injection process, but they tend to stick to the fibres of the first filter element they encounter. If this is the pre-filter, the fine filter lying downstream will be left relatively unsullied, and is therefore better able to remove what remains.

Incidentally, no matter how clean your fuel may appear, the ever-present asphaltenes will continue to clog up your filters. There couldn't be a better reason for changing them regularly. See Chapter 16 for details

THE INJECTION PROCESS

The role of injection pumps is crucial to the proper working of diesel engines. And why this should be so is easily understood, since they perform an extremely demanding job. After receiving the fuel from the lift pump they must deliver precisely metered quantities of fuel to each injector, exactly on time and at very high pressure – and they must do so over and over again.

Such is the precision of these mechanical marvels that only skilled specialists should venture inside. When it comes to self-maintenance – DON'T.

DIAGNOSTICS AND TROUBLESHOOTING

Almost every engine comes with warning devices that give notice that things are wrong. These might be gauges monitoring oil pressure, coolant temperature and battery charging, or simple lights and buzzers that will be activated if worrying thresholds are exceeded. Of equal importance to these electrical guardians are the skipper's senses of sight, sound and smell – of which the first two are by far the most important and the third the most desperate, since by then you will have missed the early signs and the engine will be seriously overheating.

Oil-pressure sensor

Smoke signals

Black or grey smoke is caused by unburned fuel and often contains soot that can settle to form a dirty patch on the water. Don't immediately suspect the engine – check for other causes first.

- Too much load on the engine. If black smoke emerges when moving from a standstill but clears very quickly, you may simply have opened the throttle too savagely. Or…

- A dirty, weed-festooned hull will cause lots of extra drag. So will towing another boat. Or…

- Too large or over-pitched prop. The engine is simply struggling to turn it. Or…

- A fouled prop. If boat speed suddenly slows this is a very likely cause. Now, to the engine…

- Dirty air filters. The engine simply isn't breathing deeply enough. Or…

- Engine space ventilation has been reduced. Look for items that might be blocking the air's path towards the engine.

- Turbo failure – again, not enough air is getting into the cylinders.

- Constriction of the exhaust system causing high back pressure. Perhaps a collapsed exhaust hose or a partially closed seacock.

- Faulty injectors or injection pump. Check everything else before you decide this is the problem. This is a job for the professionals.

Blue smoke arises from burning crankcase oil, which has reached the combustion chamber usually past worn components.

- Worn valve guides.

- Worn or seized piston rings.

- Turbo oil seal failure. Lubricating oil is escaping into the hot exhaust gases.

- Crankcase has been overfilled.

- High crankcase pressure due to blocked breather.

- Thermostat stuck open. The engine is running at below its normal operating temperature.

White 'smoke' is nearly always water vapour and is quite normal when the engine is first started. However, if it persists for more than few seconds, things could be amiss with the engine.

- Water in the fuel – most probable if the engine runs erratically.

- Cracked cylinder head casting.

- Blown head gasket. Cooling water is escaping from the galleries and entering a combustion chamber.

- Cracked exhaust manifold.

SHAKE, RATTLE AND ROLL

Although it's certainly possible that excessive vibration could be due to the engine itself, this is another situation where the cause is likely to be elsewhere.

- Bent prop shaft.

- Damaged propeller. Possibly a lost blade, particularly likely with folding and feathering props. Both this and the bent shaft become prime suspects if the prop has recently been seriously fouled by flotsam.

- Broken engine mount.

- Loose shaft coupling.

- Loose shaft anode.

- Cutless bearing failure. These rarely fail catastrophically – you usually get plenty of warning.

- Gearbox failure. If so, you should be able to hear it if you can get close enough.

- Internal engine failure, such as big end bearings, main bearings or valves. Again, this should be clearly audible.

GENERAL LACK OF PERFORMANCE

■ Marine growths on hull or prop. Even a few barnacles on the propeller blades can seriously impair their efficiency as foils. The loss of drive can be very dramatic.

■ Damaged prop – possibly a bent blade.

■ Turbo failure or accumulated dirt.

■ Blockage to the fuel system. Check the pre-filter first to make sure it's clear. You may have fallen prey to the diesel bug!

■ Cable not opening the throttle fully. It could be broken or frayed or the holding clamp (at the engine end) could have vibrated loose.

■ Engine in need of an overhaul.

■ On stern drives and sail drives the propeller bush could be slipping.

The engine hunts or dies

■ Out of fuel. Either very bad planning or your fuel gauges are faulty.

■ Fuel cock shut – perhaps partially.

■ Blocked or partially blocked filters.

■ Fuel line blocked. Suspect the diesel bug!

■ Water in fuel.

■ Fuel lift pump defective – perhaps a split diaphragm.

■ Air in the fuel. Suspect a loose connection or leaking seal somewhere.

■ Tank air vent crushed or blocked. There's a partial vacuum in the tank.

■ Split fuel line.

■ Fouled prop.

Possible mechanical causes

■ Partial engine seizure due to loss of oil or serious overheating.

■ Valves – perhaps a broken spring. Expect lots of noise.

■ Hole in piston crown.

■ Fuel injection pump problems.

■ Turbo failure. There may be billows of black smoke.

Overheating alarm sounds

At the earliest possible moment, reduce the revs, check the exhaust outlet for raw water flow and stop the engine.

If there's little or no water spurting from the exhaust it could be:

■ Seacock partially or completely shut.

■ Blocked, or partially blocked, raw water inlet or strainer.

■ Plastic bag over sail drive leg or seacock.

■ Air leak in the strainer seal – the suction is being lost and the onset of overheating is usually rapid.

■ Damaged pump impeller.

■ Split hose somewhere.

But if there's a good flow of water from the exhaust it could be:

- Thermostat failed in the closed position.

- Loss of freshwater coolant. This could be a hose, the heat exchanger or maybe even a calorifier. (Be very careful when you investigate. The evidence is probably boiling hot!)

- Slack or broken drive belt. If the belt also drives the alternator, you would also expect the battery light or alarm to be activated.

Oil warning light or alarm activated

Don't hesitate. Shut the engine down immediately. Then check for:

- Engine oil leaks.

- Crankcase oil level.

- Pressure relief valve.

- Defective sender unit or wiring.

- Big end bearing failure.

- Ruptured oil cooler.

Alternator charge alarm sounds

Stop engine and investigate. Remember the most likely cause is a broken belt which, if it's also driving the raw water pump, will mean the engine will rapidly overheat and the exhaust system could be seriously damaged by uncooled gases.

- Broken or slack drive belt.

- Defective alternator.

- Power to alternator field coils interrupted.

- Wiring fault or short circuit.

- Glow plug remaining on.

SKIPPER'S TIP

Seriously consider fitting an exhaust alarm. The sensor of the engine's alarm only works when it's surrounded by water. If there's a catastrophic loss of coolant, it becomes useless.

USEFUL READING

For the best advice on looking after a diesel engine, use the *RYA Diesel Engine Handbook* (G25)

DEPENDABLE DIESELS –
WHEN THINGS GO WRONG

Bleeding the fuel system

Assuming there hasn't been a major mechanical failure within the engine, and also that there's power (electric or manual) to crank it smartly enough to start, almost all transient diesel problems can be attributed to the fuel supply – or lack of it!

So ...

■ *Check there is fuel in the tank* ❶*.*

■ *Next, check that the filters and supply lines aren't blocked. If there's debris in the pre-filter bowl* ❸ *clear this out* **and** *replace the filter element. Even if the tank is severely contaminated, simply clearing the filter might restore the supply enough to get you home, where you can attend to the underlying problem more conveniently.*

Diesel engines are undoubtedly forgiving and dependable but one thing they won't tolerate is air in the fuel system. Air can enter for a number of reasons: running out of fuel or servicing or replacement of components – such as filter elements – being common

causes. Although some engines claim to be self-purging, most need outside intervention.

The exact sequence may vary from engine to engine, but the one described here is typical. It involves filling the system with fuel from tank to injectors, usually by manually operating the lift pump. Simple? Of course!

■ *Ensure the tank* ❶ *has plenty of fuel in it and its shut-off valve* ❷ *is open.*

■ *Try the lift pump's operating handle* ❹ *to see if it works fully. If it doesn't work at all or its stroke seems limited, give the engine half a turn (to move the operating cam) and try again.*

■ *If the fuel is drawn from the bottom of the tank and the pre-filter is below the level of the fuel (as shown here) crack open its bleed screw and it will fill by gravity. If not, keep the bleed screw closed – it's time to use the lift pump and turn your attention to the fine filter.*

■ *Open the bleed screw on the fine filter* ❺ *and pump away until bubble-free fuel emerges. Don't be astonished if this takes some time. The fuel may have to travel a fair way. When satisfied, nip up the bleed screw.*

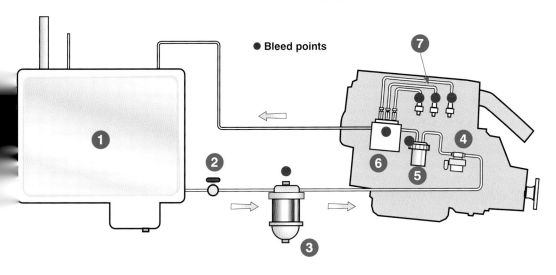

● **Bleed points**

SKIPPER'S TIP

Mark all bleed points with a blob of conspicuously coloured paint to help identify them.

This should be enough for most engines, but not for all – including most notably the GM series Yanmars, Perkins, Thorneycrofts and the various Kubota derivatives.

■ *For them, the next step is the injection pump* **6**. *Loosen the bleed screw (some older rotary injection pumps have two bleed screws and you will have to do both, starting with the lower one) and resume your labours on the lift pump. Once the fuel runs clear of bubbles, close the screw (or screws) and give the lift pump a few more strokes for good measure.*

This really should be enough. Try and start the engine in the normal way. If you fail you will have to bleed the injectors **7**. *Since these are on the high-pressure side of the injection pump, the manual lift pump won't be up to the task, so you will need to use the engine.*

■ *Loosen all the injection pump nuts at the injectors by a couple of turns.*

■ *Set the throttle to full ahead, out of gear, and turn the engine over with the ignition key. Limit yourself to no more than 15-second bursts to avoid burning out the starter motor.*

■ *First you will see the inevitable bubbles around the nuts, but these will become squirts. At which time, harden down the injectors, nuts and… start the engine!*

WARNING!!!
The pressure of the fuel emerging from the injection pipes is enough to drive it through your skin. Keep your fingers away from the nuts while the engine is turning over.

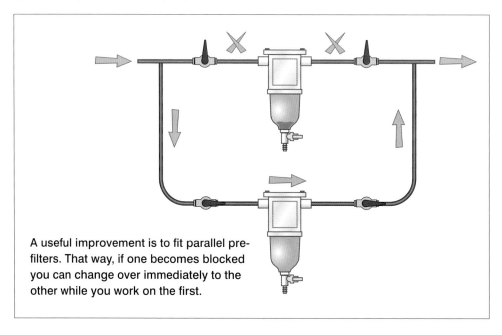

A useful improvement is to fit parallel pre-filters. That way, if one becomes blocked you can change over immediately to the other while you work on the first.

CHAPTER 16

DIY for diesel

TAKE CARE OF YOUR FUEL FILTERS

As we discussed on page 85, the ideal arrangement is to have the fuel supply run the gauntlet of a pair of filters before it reaches the engine. The first is called the pre-filter and is usually fitted remotely from the engine, somewhere accessible in the run of the fuel line. The second is known as the fine filter and is invariably mounted on the engine assembly. Although they aren't identical there are similarities, both in their construction and in the way you maintain them.

You should check your engine manual but replacement intervals of 200–300 engine hours are typical. If your fuel becomes contaminated the pre-filter will need more frequent replacement – in severe cases down to a matter of minutes! But, even if everything seems to be working well, don't be tempted to stretch the replacement schedule. The fuel might look clear but tiny particles will have been building up in the filter elements since the very first drop passed through them – and then there are those asphaltenes we came across earlier.

There are three distinct types of filter:

Replaceable element: such as RACOR® and SEPAR®

Cartridge: such as CAV®

Spin-on: such as FLEETGUARD®

Pre-filters often (and ideally) have a water trap at the bottom of the filter. Let's start there.

Draining a water trap

If your pre-filter has a transparent bowl, any water or sediment trapped in it should be clearly visible. The bowls on some filters are metal and must be drained to see what they contain. Either way, some bowls have a small stopcock; others a drain plug.

■ *Place a suitable container underneath, before opening the stopcock or loosening the plug.*

■ *Once the fuel is running clear, close the cock or screw the plug shut. Don't over-tighten the latter. It's hollow and easily damaged. Some are plastic and their threads are fragile.*

No air should have entered the system so it won't need bleeding.

Replacing filter elements

Before you disassemble any filter lying below the level in the fuel tank, make sure you close the fuel cock. If you don't you'll have an almighty mess on your hands as the tank attempts to empty itself into the bilge. Or if you are fortunate enough, or have had the foresight to fit stopcocks on the inlet and outlet side of your pre-filter, close them both. The downstream cock will stop fuel draining back from the fuel line and lift pump. Spillage will be limited and less air will enter the system.

Working tidily is important. Diesel fuel is invasive stuff and the better it is contained the happier you will be. Hang a plastic bag or put a bowl beneath the filter to catch the drips. And scatter some rags or paper towels around to absorb any splatters.

Clean off any external dirt before you go any further. You don't want it to find its way into the body of the filter as you work.

NOTE: Always disable the engine when working nearby, either by removing the key from the start switch or by disconnecting the battery. You don't want anyone firing it up while you're working on it!

Cartridge-type filters

With these the filter element is contained in a metal cylinder clamped between the filter head and a base plate. A frequent addition to the basic unit is either a glass or metal bowl fitted immediately below the cartridge. The whole assembly is held together by a bolt running down from the top of the unit.

■ *Ensure the plastic bag (or other container) is in place. You are about to release the contents of the filter into it.*

■ *Unscrew the centre bolt. The three main components will separate and the fuel will drain into the bag.*

■ *Pull off the old canister and check the sealing rings. It's not absolutely necessary to replace the upper seal every time but, since new seals come with the new filter, you might as well. If the filter has a glass or metal bowl, the seal between the bowl and the cartridge should always be changed, since it has probably stretched.*

■ *To put it all back together, simply reverse the procedure. The best way is to assemble the base plate, bowl and cartridge with all their seals in place and offer it up to the filter head as a single stack. Make sure everything has gone back in the correct order and is properly seated.*

▲ **Cartridge filter.**

■ *While holding the stack in place, insert the bolt and hand tighten — quite a fiddly job. Finally, nip up the bolt firmly but not too savagely with a spanner.*

Many filters of this type have a removable screw plug in the head casting which allows you to top them up them with fuel before bleeding the remaining small air bubbles from the system.

Replaceable element filters

These are normally found on larger engines. Access to the elements is through a removable lid on the top — either secured with a central T-handle bolt or four small screws.

■ *First open the drain cock and take a small sample of fuel. If the fuel is clear, you won't have to empty the whole bowl, which makes life easier.*

■ *Undo the T-handle bolt or screws and lift off the lid. The fuel level should be close to the top.*

■ *Slowly lift out the old element, avoiding spillage as much as possible. Some filters of this type will have a sprung plastic cage that must be taken out first. Make a careful note of which way up it goes.*

■ *Equally slowly insert the new element into the filter housing. It will absorb fuel as it becomes immersed. If there was a cage, replace that as well.*

■ *Check the lid's sealing ring or gasket and the O-ring under the T-handle (if there is one). Fit a new one if in any doubt.*

■ *Replace the lid and secure.*

If this operation is done carefully, you shouldn't need to bleed the system at all. But if it had been necessary to drain the

unit because of contaminants, or if there had been any other significant spillage, it's possible to refill the filter from a small can before refitting the lid — again, averting the need to bleed.

Spin-on filters

The changing procedure is effectively the same as for spin-on oil filters. The fuel system must be bled after the change.

SKIPPER'S TIP

Never leave oil spills in the bilge where they might be pumped out with the bilge water. Mop up every drop you can. Use a bilge sock – these only absorb hydrocarbons – or fit an inline bilge filter to stop oil being pumped out.

CHANGING THE OIL AND FILTER

It can't be over-emphasised how important it is to maintain the quality of the lubricating oil. And don't judge it by its colour. That dark grey gloop that emerges on the end of your dipstick is no cause for panic. The oil got that way within hours of being poured into the engine. The change in colour is simply due to detergents and combustion by-products and is entirely normal.

The best way to know that your engine oil is in good condition is to follow the replacement schedule recommended by the manufacturer. Some manufacturers recommend an oil change every 150 engine hours or at the end of each season (whichever comes first) with a fresh filter every 300 hours – i.e. every second oil change. But many engineers claim that, in view of their relatively low cost, it makes more sense to replace the filter every time you change the oil. That way, there's no danger of forgetting where you are in the schedule and the two jobs can be regarded as one.

As with the fuel filters, arm yourself with plastic bags and rags – and a pair of rubber gloves, since this is messy work. Also, consult your engine manual to establish both the correct grade of oil and the quantity needed.

Extracting the old oil

- *Run the engine for 10–15 minutes, preferably in gear, to bring it up to its normal operating temperature. This will thin the oil and stir any sludge in the sump into suspension.*

- *Extract the oil. Some engines can be drained, either through a cock or by removing a sump plug. More often, the oil must be pumped out, either by way of a pre-fitted pump, or out through the dipstick tube. A piston-type pump with a thin plastic tube capable of reaching the bottom of the sump can be used, but the easiest and cleanest way is to use a vacuum-type extractor which draws the oil into its own container. When buying such an extractor, make sure it has the capacity to hold all the oil in one go.*

- *Be careful. Remember the oil is very hot.*

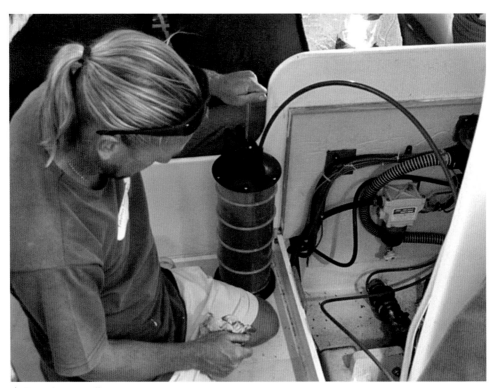

▲ **Pumping out oil.**

Replacing the filter

These are usually of the spin-on type, but larger engines may have cartridge filters (without drain bowls) in which case you should refer back to page 96.

■ *Use a filter wrench to unscrew the filter until it's just hand tight — that's to say, before any oil leaks out.*

■ *Place a plastic bag around the filter and continue to undo it while oil drains into the bag. As soon as it comes free, put the bag and filter safely in a bucket.*

■ *Remove any packaging from the new filter and check that the seals are in place.*

■ *Smear oil around the seal and screw on the replacement, being careful not to cross-thread it. Do it up as tight as possible by hand. If you're strong enough, this might be enough. If not, nip it up with the wrench but don't overtighten it — you may be the unfortunate person who has to take it off next time!*

Refill the oil

Check your engine handbook to determine the grade and quantity of oil required. Since you probably haven't got every drop of old oil out of the sump, you may find you need a little less.

▲ **You may have to improvise an extension tube to fill the gearbox oil. This one is simple – a piece of pipe and the top of a plastic bottle.**

■ *Open the oil filler and wipe away any dirt before arranging a rag around it to confine spillage.*

■ *Pour in the oil, slowing as you approach the recommended amount. Check the dipstick frequently after allowing the oil time to work its way down to the crankcase.*

Changing gearbox oil

Since there are no combustion by-products, the oil in the gearbox should remain clean. If the oil has turned black, there may be a problem: the oil could be overheating, due to a faulty clutch. If the oil has emulsified — i.e. turned a milky colour — it could be that sea water is leaking in through the oil cooler. If that's the case, don't run the engine. Get it checked by an engineer.

But, let's assume everything looks normal. Gather together the usual mopping-up implements and check in your manual for the type and quantity of the oil. Some gearboxes take the same oil as the engine; others use automatic transmission fluid (ATF).

■ *Remove the dipstick.*

■ *Extract the old oil, using the same pump as for the engine (see page 98).*

Oil level measured from here →

■ *Pour in the new oil, checking the level with the dipstick. It's usual not to screw the dipstick in when you do this. The correct reading is from the bottom of the thread.*

■ *When satisfied, replace the dipstick and nip it up tight.*

CHANGING OR ADJUSTING THE ALTERNATOR BELT

Reinforced rubber belts are an effective way of transmitting power from one part of the engine to another. They are used for a variety of purposes – the most common being to spin the alternator. Often, a single belt will be called upon to perform more than one task, perhaps driving the raw water pump as well. And, since their workings are entirely external, they are exceptionally easy to inspect and maintain. In short, there are few excuses for allowing them to deteriorate to the point of failure.

The most common type of belt on smaller engines is trapezoidal in section – shaped like an equilateral triangle with the point cut off. These are called 'V' belts and they run in pulleys having tapered grooves. The belts are tensioned so they wedge into the grooves, thereby receiving the grip that prevents them slipping.

Larger engines will probably have flat (sometimes called 'serpentine') belts which are both wider and thinner than V belts.

If belts are tensioned too much, they will impart side loads on the pulleys. This will lead to accelerated wear to their bearings. If the tension is too loose, there won't be enough grip and the belt will slip and the rubber will be worn away. If you see deposits of black dust anywhere in the region, it's a sure sign of belt wear.

The object, therefore, is to get the tension exactly right – fortunately, an easy trick to master. To check a V belt's tension, press on its longest span. You should be able to deflect it about 10–12mm (approximately half an inch). The way to test a flat belt is to grip it between thumb and forefinger and try to twist it through 90°. If it twists too easily, the belt is too slack.

While you're about it, look out for fraying or other problems. Remember that if an alternator belt fails, battery charging ceases. More seriously, if the belt also drives the raw water pump, the flow stops and the engine could overheat and seize. If in doubt, replace the belt immediately – a job that should take no more than a couple of minutes.

Let's assume the belt tension is too slack and you want to tighten it.

- *Belt tension is adjusted by moving the alternator either towards or away from the engine. The alternator pivots on a supporting bracket and is braced with a slotted (and often curved) strut clamped into place with an adjustment bolt.*

- *To relax the tension, slacken – but don't remove – the bolts securing the alternator, including the one on the engine end of the slotted strut.*

With V belts you should be able to deflect the longest span 10–12mm.

With flat belts you should be able to twist the belt through 90°.

■ If the belt is damaged and you've decided to replace it, first remove the old one. Pivot the alternator in as far as it will go towards the engine and roll the belt out of the groove. Take time to inspect and clean the pulleys − particularly of any rust (which is abrasive) or grease (slippery).

■ Now fit the new belt, first over the flywheel pulley then over any others, leaving the alternator till last. You may find it helps to slowly rotate the flywheel by hand, while easing that final bight over the rim and into its groove.

■ The alternator must be pulled away from the engine to re-tension the belt, and this is best achieved using a short length of wood − try a hammer handle − to give you a bit of leverage. Wedge your lever between the engine block and the alternator and pull outwards. Tighten the various bolts, starting with the ones on the strut.

■ Check the tension as before, and again after two or three hours running. A new belt may stretch a little.

CHANGING A THERMOSTATIC VALVE

Engine thermostats are not items that need servicing. They either work or they don't. When they fail, they must be replaced.

▲ **If the thermostat fails it must be replaced.**

If the engine overheats and water still spurts from the exhaust, it's a fair bet that the thermostat has failed in the closed position. However, if you find blue smoke coming from the exhaust, there's a possibility that the engine is running too cool because the thermostat has stuck open. The first situation is the most common and demands immediate attention. Thermostats only rarely fail open. If they do, you can be rather more relaxed about when you deal with it.

Removing a thermostat is a fairly simple matter.

■ Identify the housing − typically dome-shaped and close to the forward end of the cylinder head.

■ The top of the housing is usually held down with a couple of bolts. Undo them.

■ Lift out the old thermostat and replace with new. Alternatively, test the old one as described in the next section. If it's still working properly you may want to continue using it.

■ Reassemble, making sure that all gaskets go back as before.

TESTING A THERMOSTAT

If the valve is jammed open when you remove it, you will know immediately that it's defective. If it's closed you can perform a simple test to see whether it's working or not.

Immerse the thermostat in a saucepan of water and heat it on the galley stove. It should start to open at around 75°C to 85°C (167°F to 185°F) − a range well short of boiling point. If the water boils and the valve stays shut, it's clearly faulty.

RENEWING THE FRESH WATER COOLANT

The role of antifreeze is broader than the term would suggest. As well as guarding against frost damage, almost all antifreezes contain rust and corrosion inhibitors that help protect the system. The effectiveness of these additives reduces with time, so the coolant should be replaced every year, regardless of whether or not there's a risk of freezing.

▲ **When the engine is cool, the coolant level should be somewhere between the two ridged lines.**

■ *Remove the pressure cap from the filler.*

■ *Locate the drain cocks — there's often more than one. Place a bowl underneath and open the cocks one by one until they run dry. Don't drain the coolant into the bilge and pump it out later. Ethylene glycol-based antifreezes are very toxic. (Polypropylene glycol is much safer but, unfortunately, more expensive which discourages its use.)*

■ *Once the system is empty close the cocks. The proportion of antifreeze to water depends on the lowest temperature that might occur in your area. There*

should be details of recommended mix ratios with the antifreeze. Err on the generous side if you want. Your engine manual will tell you the total capacity of the system, so it's a fairly easy matter to work out how much of the final mix you will need.

■ *Pour the antifreeze into the engine first, then top up with water.*

■ *Run the engine for about 30 minutes to mix the two together.*

■ *Check the coolant level again once it has cooled down. Top up again as necessary. Dispose of antifreeze at your marina or take to your local household recycling centre.*

> # WARNING!
> Never remove the filler cap while the engine is hot. Remember, the coolant is under pressure and serious scalds can be caused by steam and water bursting out.

REPLACE RAW WATER PUMP IMPELLER

This could either be a routine check or because the raw water flow has stopped. In the latter case the engine is overheating and you will doubtless have shut it down. You've checked the cooling water inlet strainer and it's clear of obstructions. The next most obvious culprit is the raw water pump — or, more specifically, the rubber impeller it contains.

■ *Undo the screws and remove the pump's face plate.*

■ *The impeller might look intact but it pays to take a closer look to be sure. Grip one of its vanes with a pair of needle nose pliers and pull it out. Alternatively — or if all the vanes are missing! — use a pair of screwdrivers to lever it out. Be careful to*

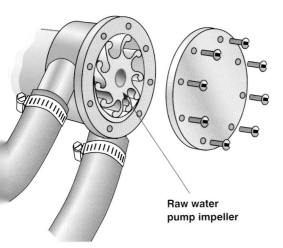

**Raw water
pump impeller**

avoid damaging the edges of the brass casting. It helps to wrap the screwdriver shanks in masking tape to cushion them.

■ *With the impeller extracted, examine it closely – particularly the vane roots. If you find any cracks, discard it.*

■ *If there are vanes missing, they have to have gone somewhere. They might have been pumped upwards towards the heat exchanger but, equally, they could have dropped back into the suction tube. Whatever it takes, hunt them down until they are all accounted for. To draw them through a new impeller could be to undo all your good work.*

■ *Clean all traces of the old paper gasket from the face of the housing.*

■ *Smear the new impeller lightly with washing-up liquid and slide it back onto its shaft, making sure the pin (or grub screw) engages properly with the slot and that the vanes trail backwards from the direction of rotation.*

■ *Fit a new gasket and replace the face plate. Tighten the screws evenly in rotation.*

▲ **An impeller puller is a useful tool to have on board.**

REPLACING ENGINE ANODES

All raw water cooled engines will have one or more sacrificial zinc anodes screwed into their blocks somewhere. Many indirectly cooled engines also have anodes in their various heat exchangers.

The anode's role in life is to reduce the electrolytic corrosion that occurs when metals are in contact with an electrolyte – in this case sea water. The zinc wastes away so that more important components will survive. Unfortunately, they waste away unseen, with no external sign that they have become depleted.

The engine manual will tell you how many there are and how often they must be changed – every year is typical. The manual will also tell you where they are located, which is very helpful since they aren't exactly conspicuous.

■ Replacing an anode is simply a matter of unscrewing it and popping in a new one.

CARE OF AIR FILTERS

It's all too easy to neglect air filters. The relatively dust-free environments in which we keep our boats tends to make us unconcerned. And yet the gradual build-up of particles does happen – an insidious process that gradually chokes off the air and robs our engines of power.

Maintenance will depend on what type of air filter you have. The alternatives are:

■ **Paper element.** These can't be rejuvenated. Simply throw away the old one when it becomes clogged and replace it with new.

■ **Synthetic wadding** – usually trapped in a metal or plastic cage. These can be washed out in a water and detergent solution. Allow to dry before refitting.

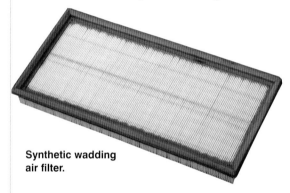

Synthetic wadding air filter.

■ **Oil bath type.** Very much yesterday's technology. A screen made up of coarse strands of metal is positioned over a shallow reservoir of oil which mists upwards to leave a sticky deposit on the screen. The reservoir should be emptied and cleaned periodically. Flush the screen out in diesel fuel or paraffin (kerosene) to remove particles stuck to it.

CHAPTER 17

Stern gear

Naturally, the power provided by the engine is of no propulsive value unless it can be transmitted to the water. Logically enough, this task falls first to the transmission, in the form of a gearbox, and then to the 'stern gear', which is all the paraphernalia aft of the shaft coupling.

The simplest, and by far the commonest arrangement for sailing boats and traditional-type motor vessels, is to use a straight shaft that exits through a waterproof 'stern gland' and carries a propeller at its aft-most extremity. Figure 17.1 shows a typical installation.

Let's start with the prop and work our way forward.

PROPELLERS

The almost exclusive material of choice here is bronze, but here we must be cautious. Bronze is an alloy made principally of copper and tin and it is very resistant to corrosion. But most propellers are made of 'manganese bronze' – a somewhat deceptive phrase – meaning an alloy which contains about 40 per cent zinc. More correctly it should be described as a high-strength brass.

The reason the distinction is important is that brass is susceptible to 'dezincification' – that word meaning a form of corrosion in which the zinc in the alloy is gradually consumed by galvanic action, leaving a soft and structurally useless copper residue behind. The first signs of dezincification are pink patches on blade surfaces, with material being lost as deterioration progresses. Wherever the metal is thinnest will be eaten away first and it's not unusual to find blades crumbling away around their edges.

The whole subject of both galvanic and electrolytic corrosion is covered at length in the next chapter – including how you can combat its effects.

Because of the higher structural

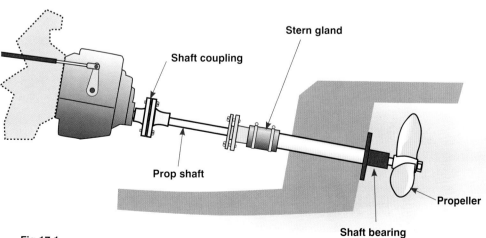

Stern gland

Shaft coupling

Prop shaft

Shaft bearing

Propeller

Fig 17.1

▲ **A three-bladed folding propeller.**

demands placed on them, folding and feathering props are almost invariably made of aluminium bronze or nickel aluminium bronze – both greatly superior (and more costly) than manganese bronze.

Maintenance:

It takes very little fouling to reduce the efficiency of a propeller. Just a scattering of barnacles and a few strands of weed can affect performance dramatically. Indeed, a heavily fouled propeller may develop no drive at all. Folding props can even fail to open and the blades of the feathering type may become restricted in their movement or seized solid. There are proprietary propeller antifoulings but reports as to their efficacy are mixed. I rely on a scraper and a lungful of air, myself.

There's little else you can do for fixed props other than protect them (as far as you're able) from galvanic corrosion – see next chapter. But folding and feathering props should be stripped, cleaned and lubricated (with waterproof grease) about once a year, if possible.

The servicing procedure – typically a fairly easy task – depends upon the make of the prop and you should obtain the appropriate instructions from the manufacturer.

SHAFTS

Bronze propeller shafts were once common but stainless steel is the overwhelming favourite today. And a generally durable substance it has proved.

The two threats to shafts are corrosion and wear and, to some extent, they are likely to occur in roughly the same areas. This is because stainless steel is made stainless because the chromium content in the alloy forms a 'passivated' oxide layer on the surface – but only in the presence of oxygen. When submerged, the oxygen is provided by the surrounding water but, if the water stagnates – meaning it has difficulty replenishing itself – the dissolved oxygen is rapidly used up and the oxide layer breaks down. The result is known as 'crevice corrosion' and it can do great damage.

For a stainless prop shaft there are a couple of areas where the water is prone to stagnation: within the stern tube and inside any submerged bearings. For most of us it's not a major threat, which is just as well, because there's not much we can do about it.

Incidentally, both aluminium and titanium are also prone to crevice corrosion.

SHAFT BEARINGS

We can't talk about wear without referring to bearings. Water-lubricated 'cutless' (sometimes wrongly called 'cutlass') bearings are now virtually universal. They consist of a tubular shell – usually brass but sometimes phenolic or GRP – containing a fluted rubber liner. The name derives from their ability to flush away abrasive particles – such as sand – before it can damage either the shaft or the bearing's surface.

Of course where there's friction, however slight, there's always wear but this can be minimised by…

■ Ensuring correct alignment of the shaft – meaning, in reality, the engine alignment. Because cutless bearings are very forgiving by nature, it's all too easy to get away with even quite large degrees of misalignment. If you find your cutless bearing is wearing out rapidly, check that the shaft is running concentrically through it (see Figure 17.2).

Realigning an engine is quite a skilled job, best entrusted to an engineer.

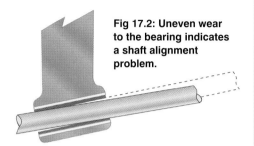

Fig 17.2: Uneven wear to the bearing indicates a shaft alignment problem.

■ Also ensure that there is a generous water flow through the bearing. A common mistake is to fit shaft anodes too close to the bearing, thereby obstructing the flow. Intermediate bearings – often fitted on larger boats where the shaft exits the hull – should have a water feed into the stern tube forward of the bearing.

STERN GLANDS

This is an area which has seen a flurry of development over the last few years, with a number of proprietary stern glands appearing on the market. But there are still an enormous number of the traditional packed glands (also inelegantly known as 'stuffing boxes') still doing sterling work.

Packed glands are nothing more than a pair of concentric cylinders, one inside the other (see Figure 17.3). Basically, three or four rings of packing material are compressed between an internal shoulder (machined inside the outer casing) and the end of the inner compressor tube which is pressed down onto the packing, either by a threaded collar or (as shown here) with a couple of machine screws pulling down on protruding flanges. The latter is the better arrangement, being much easier to adjust.

The packing material is most commonly of square-sectioned braided flax, but there are also a number of synthetic materials, all claiming their own advantages. The gland is lubricated with a water-resistant grease – often supplied by a 'remote greaser' – and, to a great extent, by the water itself. For that last reason, it's important to note that packed glands are intended to leak. Not copiously, mind. Two or three drips a minute is quite enough.

Packed glands are often attached to the stern tube with a short length of rubber hose. This allows the gland to move with the engine, reducing the side loads that would otherwise occur. Clearly, failure of the hose would cause catastrophic leakage. Bearing in mind the trifling costs involved, it makes

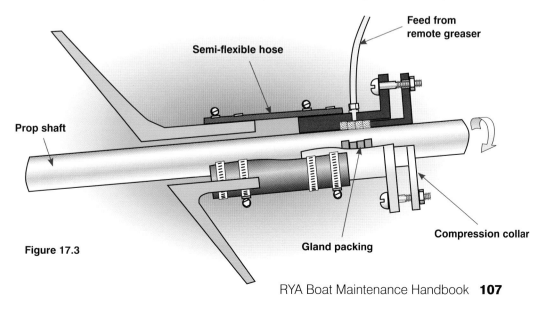

Feed from remote greaser

Semi-flexible hose

Prop shaft

Compression collar

Gland packing

Figure 17.3

sense to replace it, and the hose clips that secure it, every time the shaft is drawn.

Maintenance:

■ *Make sure the gland doesn't run short of grease. Most skippers apply some sort of routine to greasing – one turn of the grease cup or remote greaser for every eight engine hours, for example.*

Adjusting a packed gland

Assuming the stuffing box was set up correctly in the first place, it can only become looser with wear. The first signs may be an increase in the drip rate, but this can be masked by squeezing in more grease. A more reliable indication is the remote greaser itself. As the packing wears away, the contact between the shaft and the packing gets slacker, and the task of screwing down the handle becomes easier. To confirm your suspicions take a look below. If anything more than traces of grease are exuding from the stuffing box, the gland needs adjustment.

■ *With the engine stopped and out of gear, wipe away any excess grease and rotate the shaft by hand. It probably turns too freely – though this is a matter of judgement and difficult to define.*

■ *After backing off any lock nuts, tighten the adjustment screws (or threaded collar) a fraction of a turn – and, of course, equally since the compression must be even. It's advisable to proceed in small increments, so you don't have to ease off later.*

■ *Try turning the shaft again. There should be some resistance, but not a lot. Remember, better too little than too much. Count the drips: anywhere between one and five per minute will do fine.*

■ *When you think you've got it right, tighten any lock nuts and run the engine in gear for ten minutes or so. Then go below and feel the stuffing box. It should be quite cool to the touch. If it is hot, it has been over-tightened and must be slackened a little.*

Note: Although not ideal, stuffing boxes can be adjusted with the boat ashore where, of course, there will be no tell-tale drips to guide you. This means you must judge by the rotational resistance of the shaft alone. Squirt some washing-up liquid into the cutless bearing to prevent any friction there from deceiving you.

Repacking a stern gland

There comes a point when no amount of adjustment will do, and you must face the fact that the gland packing needs replacing. This is a job which, for obvious reasons, should never be attempted afloat!

Here's how:

■ *Remove the adjustment screws or collar from the stuffing box and slide the compressor part forward up the prop shaft.*

■ *The next stage is fiddly. The old packing has to be hooked out of its recess. A good trick is to use a woodscrew – preferably a brass one to avoid scratching the shaft – that you screw into the packing, then pull out with pliers. A small bradawl and bits of bent wire might also come in handy. Make sure that all of the packing is removed.*

■ *Measure the gap between the shaft and the inside of the casing. This will indicate the size (meaning thickness) of the packing you will need. These measurements could well be in imperial units – i.e. fractions of an inch – though new packing material may be sold in equivalent metric sizes. For example a 6.5mm packing would replace one of a ¼ inch. The length of each piece, of course, will equal the circumference of the shaft.*

■ *To cut the new packing to size, wrap it around the prop shaft the appropriate number of times, making sure there are no twists in it. Then take a very sharp knife and slice lengthways along the coil so the packing is cut into individual pieces. You don't need to crawl into the engine space to do this. Choose an easily accessible bit of the shaft — even outside the boat as it's ashore.*

▲ **When cutting packing rings it helps to have an odd length of shaft to work on.**

■ *Smear each piece of packing with grease, curl them around the shaft and tamp them into the recess, ensuring they sit squarely on the shaft and that their cut ends don't coincide. If there are four rings in total, you may find it helpful to temporarily assemble and tighten down the compressor tube and its securing mechanism after the third ring. This will consolidate the packing and make room for the last one.*

▲ Stern gland packing rings.

■ *Reassemble the stuffing box and rotate the shaft several times to help the packing bed down. It should turn freely. The final adjustment is best left until the boat is afloat. Hang a very conspicuous sign somewhere to remind you!*

MODERN SHAFT SEALS

▲ **A modern lip seal-type gland.**

There are a number of alternatives to old-fashioned glands, and it's easy to understand why these upstarts are gaining ground. Once fitted and adjusted, they need much less attention, and are entirely drip-free. They are also a lot less messy than the older variety.

To keep the water at bay, modern stern glands rely on one of two things. The first are 'lip seals', similar in many ways to the oil seals to be found at each end of your engine's crankshaft. A flexible rubber lip bears on the shaft, pointing upstream towards the water so the hydrostatic pressure works to keep it in contact. The water also lubricates the seal, though some manufacturers advise squirting in tiny amounts of grease periodically to give it a helping hand.

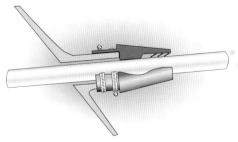

Another form of lip seal gland. Since this is a one-piece unit it must be replaced periodically.

The second group are known as 'face seals'. With these a graphite ring presses against a stainless steel collar that rotates with the shaft. Contact between the ring and the collar is maintained by a compressed rubber bellows that acts like a spring. Again, the lubricant is water.

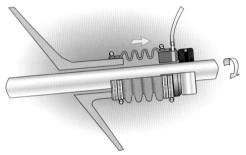

A face seal-type gland.

It's vital to keep both lip and face seals constantly lubricated. If starved of water for more than a few moments they will overheat and destroy themselves. This is rarely a problem at low speeds since a stern gland will be permanently flooded. But, over about 12 knots, the water rushing past the after end of a stern tube can develop a strong enough venturi effect to suck it literally dry. The solution is to divert water from the engine's raw water systems and inject it directly into the glands.

Maintenance:
Virtually none but this should be noted:

■ *Every time a boat is re-launched, Volvo-type lip seal glands should have any trapped air bled from them to make sure they don't run dry. This takes only a few seconds and is done by simply pressing the gland to one side by hand until water emerges.*

■ *Also, every 200 hours of running time they should be lubricated by squirting grease under the seals with a toothpaste tube-type applicator.*

INTEGRATED DRIVE UNITS

There are advantages to be had in combining the entire propulsion system into a single compact unit. That way the manufacturers take the whole process under their control, ensuring there are no weaknesses or incompatibilities anywhere in the power train. The boatbuilders simply take the unit out of its box and bolt it into the place prepared for it. The engine, transmission and final drive are installed, literally within minutes, without any of the tricky alignment procedures associated with conventional installations.

Stern drives

As well as the other advantages integrated drive units bring, stern drives are steerable so bring the added advantage that you can dispense with conventional rudder systems completely. Otherwise known as 'inboard outboards' or 'outdrives', they reign supreme on small to mid-size power craft. Each complete assembly pierces and is attached to the transom, with a 'drive leg' outside the hull and the engine inside. Waterproof bellows allow the two to work together without admitting water into the boat.

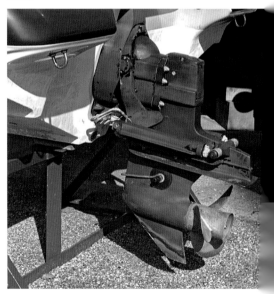

▲ **A typical stern drive unit.**

The drive leg contains the gearbox and a system of bevel gears to crank the output around two 90° corners. As well as steering, they can be tilted up and down to reduce draught and adjust fore and aft trim.

Sail drives

Popular on small to mid-size yacht auxiliaries, a 'sail drive' is a relatively simple device that can be neither steered nor tilted. The drive leg passes through a strong rubber diaphragm that isolates the engine vibrations from the hull while keeping the water at bay. Some models have twin diaphragms with an electronic leak sensor between.

Maintenance:

Needless to say both types are relatively complex pieces of machinery, the servicing of which should be left to the professionals. But there are a few things you can attend to.

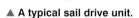

▲ **A typical sail drive unit.**

■ *On stern drives, the bellows should be inspected for cracks regularly. If water is allowed to enter it can do serious and expensive damage to the universal joints they protect.*

■ *Replace any anodes when they are about 50 per cent depleted. The various castings are of aluminium alloy and are very susceptible to galvanic corrosion.*

WARNING!

Cuprous oxide-based antifoulings can cause serious galvanic corrosion to aluminium drive units. NEVER use them for this purpose. However, cuprous thiocyanate antifoulings can be used but even then only over compatible primers. Consult manufacturers' data sheets for precise application details.

CHAPTER 18

Corrosion protection

In the context of corrosion the words 'galvanic' and 'electrolytic' are frequently misunderstood or thought to be interchangeable, so let's deal with this first.

- Galvanic corrosion occurs when two dissimilar metals are immersed in an electrolyte and connected by a conductor. This creates a 'galvanic cell', a very simple form of battery in which the negative 'cathode' remains intact and the positive 'anode' is eaten away. A bronze prop on a stainless steel shaft is an example, as is a stainless steel stanchion in a cast aluminium socket. All it takes is a little seawater to start them fizzing.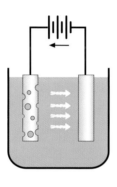

- Electrolytic corrosion results from an electric current from an external source (often accidental leakage) impressing itself on two immersed metallic objects. In this case the metals can be identical, since the potential difference is imposed by the current itself, with the identity of cathode and anode being determined by the polarity of the current. Once again, the anode becomes the unfortunate victim.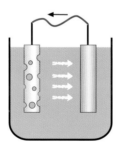

Sacrificial anodes: Galvanic corrosion can be countered by deliberately introducing a strongly anodic metal which sacrifices itself to protect objects more cathodic than itself. The chosen sacrifice – usually of zinc or, less commonly, aluminium – comes in various forms. Some are bolted to the hull and bonded internally to vulnerable components (engines, shafts and P-struts being notable) and some are attached directly to the object they seek to protect (shafts, trim tabs etc).

Impressed current: Yet another method employs deliberate electrolytic intervention. The lowly zinc is replaced by a nobler metal and a small current is introduced to counter the direction of the galvanic flow. Impressed current systems are very popular on large commercial vessels, where the frequent replacement of anodes is impracticable. On pleasure craft they are used chiefly to protect highly vulnerable machinery such as aluminium alloy-encased drive legs and jet drives.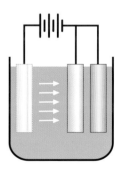

Planning any cathodic protection system should be done thoughtfully and with restraint. Isolated components such as bronze seacocks (when secured with bronze bolts or attached to bronze through hull fittings) shouldn't be connected, because to do so might create galvanic cells where none existed before.

WARNING: This is not really relevant for modern boats but it's worth noting that care should be taken not to over-protect wooden-hulled vessels. Traditional boatbuilding timbers such as oak and mahogany are naturally acidic but localised galvanic action can make them alkaline, destroying the lignin that binds the fibres together (the process is known as delignification). Softening of planking around anodes and seacocks is a very common fault caused by this process.

Anodes will also provide protection against electrolytic attack but the length of time they can hold out against such assaults depends on the strength of the currents involved. Once any anodes have been depleted, the most anodic components that remain will be targeted next.

And it needn't be your fault. Even if you're scrupulous about guarding your own electrical systems against leakage , you can still fall victim to the carelessness or misfortune of others. Marinas are notorious breeding grounds for rogue currents, either from neighbouring boats or from the pontoons themselves. Observe the similarity between the situation illustrated here and that of the galvanic and electrolytic cells. It's easy to see how other people's problems can become your own – unseen and often expensive.

EARTH LOOPS

Figure 18.1 shows two yachts, both properly connected to the shore power. In compliance with recommended practice, each has its AC and DC grounds bonded together. Neither is actually drawing power from the pontoon but this doesn't matter. The earth wire continues to link them together, binding them into a galvanic relationship in which the most anodic boat will suffer damage. Leakage currents will make the situation even worse.

Luckily, it's possible to block the path for tiny DC currents to escape while still allowing full AC fault currents to run safely to earth – yet few boats fit such protection as standard. There are two ways of achieving this:

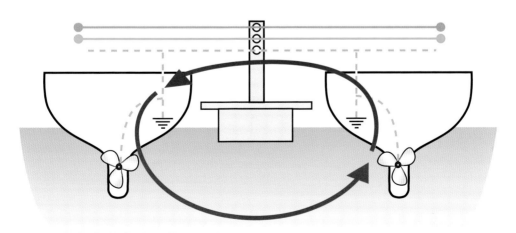

Figure 18.1

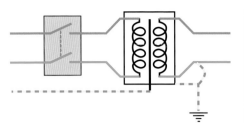

Isolation transformers: Although heavy and relatively expensive, these should be seriously considered for larger vessels with elaborate AC systems and those with conductive hulls – i.e. aluminium, steel or carbon fibre composite. Here there's no direct connection with the shore supply. The power is transferred by induction from one coil to another. A boat ground plate is necessary to maintain the neutral at earth potential but at least there are no polarity problems since isolation transformers don't care which way round the shore power arrives.

■ **Galvanic isolator:** Lighter and less costly, these are a good choice for simpler systems. A pair of diodes are arranged in parallel. An AC current will pass straight through – in or out – while a low voltage DC current will find one diode barring its way entirely while the voltage drop (typically about 0.7V) across the diode will negate its effect if coming in the opposite direction.

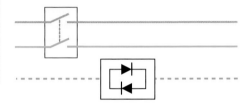

CHAPTER 19

DC electrics

Batteries can be divided into two separate camps – those that can be recharged and those that can't. Those that can't are known as 'primary cell batteries' and depend upon chemical processes that become irreversibly exhausted once the active ingredients are spent. In practical terms this means that we use these 'batteries' until they are dead, then throw them away – with care, since some of their constituents are toxic.

Extremely useful though primary cells are – powering torches, portable radios and the like – of more importance to seafarers are the rechargeable batteries that 'store' the electricity we use to power our onboard systems. These are made up of 'secondary cells' connected in series. Of course, secondary cells don't actually store anything. What they do is convert electrical energy into a form of chemical energy that can be released whenever we need it to provide a current. And they can do it **over and over again.**

BATTERIES

It isn't essential to know how batteries work, it but it helps to know something about the different types.

Automotive batteries

These are almost certainly the type we are most familiar with. We turn a key, the starter motor cranks over and our car bursts into life. Now, starter motors are muscular beasts. And hungry. They need a lot of current and need it fast – but only for a few seconds before they are recharged by the engine's alternator.

▲ **Engine start battery.**

Automotive batteries are designed specifically for the job. Each cell contains a large number of very thin plates, presenting the maximum amount of surface area to the electrolyte. This enables them to release large currents extremely quickly.

But there's a price to pay for this. If deeply discharged – say by the sustained loads demanded of a boat's domestic system – their fragile plates will soon buckle, the active material will be dislodged from their grids and fall to the bottom of the casing where it will short-circuit the plates. The battery will be dead. Permanently.

Automotive-type batteries have no place on a boat, other than perhaps to start engines. And even that is debatable.

Deep cycle batteries

These are sometimes called 'traction' batteries because they are often used on milk floats, golf carts, invalid chairs and the like – all of which need electrical power to be delivered hour after hour.

The term 'deep cycle' means to

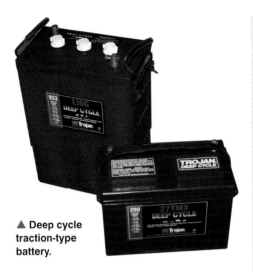

▲ Deep cycle traction-type battery.

Leisure battery.

discharge a battery to a level well below its fully charged state. But that doesn't mean dead flat. All batteries suffer every time they are cycled – some much more than others. For example, to discharge repeatedly a starter-type battery to 50 per cent would destroy it after only a few dozen cycles. On the other hand a dedicated deep cycle battery might withstand 1000 or more cycles before it met the same fate, and perhaps twice that number if only allowed to discharge to 20 per cent.

The main reason that deep cycle batteries are more durable is simple: their plates are thicker, usually of thicker solid lead, and there are far fewer of them. The downside of this arrangement is that since the plates release the current relatively slowly, they are not good at delivering lots of current in a hurry. This makes them hopeless for engine starting.

SKIPPER'S TIP

CAUTION: When it comes to deep cycling, beware of optimistic claims. If possible, check the manufacturers' specifications before choosing.

'Leisure'-type batteries

These are a compromise between starting and deep cycle batteries and popular on boats which only carry a single battery or where the electrical demands are modest. They are punchy enough to start smaller engines and can withstand some deep cycling but they perform neither role as satisfactorily as the specialised types and will not have the long service life of true deep cyclers.

Sealed lead-acid (SLA) batteries

All of the preceding batteries have liquid electrolyte sloshing about inside vented containers. Not a great idea on boats which inevitably get tossed around a bit. It's one thing to break some crockery in a knockdown – quite another to let sulphuric acid loose in your bilges. So, to have sealed batteries has obvious merits.

The word 'sealed' needs qualification. All lead-acid batteries generate gaseous hydrogen and oxygen when charging – much of which is reabsorbed in the more sophisticated types. However, if overcharged even the best of them can suffer build-ups of pressure which must be released through special safety valves before they explode. This is a one-way process. Gases can escape, nothing can get in.

Gel cell batteries

These have been around for over thirty years and are deservedly popular. The feature that distinguishes them from wet lead-acid batteries is that the liquid electrolyte has been converted into a gel by adding colloidal silica (silicon dioxide). The combination of a sealed casing and a viscous electrolyte adds up to an effectively spill-proof battery.

Gel cells can be used for starting smaller engines but they are better suited to the somewhat more tranquil role of supporting domestic services. Treated properly, they can be very long-lived, but they do need special charging regimes to keep them in good shape.

Absorbed Glass Mat (AGM) batteries

So far as construction is concerned, the name says it all. Inside you would find that the battery plates are interleaved with fine-stranded glass mats that hold the electrolyte in place by capillary action. This most recent of all lead-acid technologies was first developed for the none-but-the-best spheres of aviation and the military.

AGM batteries have very low internal

▲ AGM batteries.

resistance. This makes them super-fast when it comes both to accepting and delivering current. In other words, they can be charged very rapidly and will also deliver the quick punch of power needed to turn over engines. However, they can be damaged by high charging voltages, so the charging regime must be properly controlled.

They are not cheap.

BATTERY MONITORING

To cycle repeatedly a 12V battery down to 10.5V would soon see it on the scrap heap. To be on the safe side we should consider 11.7V to be the absolute limit – i.e. dead flat. But even this is undesirable. Over the years a fair amount of experience has been gained and it's generally agreed that to discharge to 50 per cent (of full charge) to 12.2V is a sensible trade-off between usefulness and battery life, though to set the limit to 75 per cent of full charge (12.4V) would be even better.

This means we need to keep an eye on the charge state of our batteries.

Hydrometer

For flooded, unsealed batteries, one method is to monitor the changing Specific Gravity (SG) of the electrolyte. Sulphuric acid has an SG of 1.83, meaning it's 1.83 times heavier than water (SG 1.0). When the two are combined to form the electrolyte, the SG strikes a compromise somewhere around the 1.27 mark. As a battery discharges, the sulphuric acid is progressively taken up by the chemical changes, while the water content of the electrolyte increases. By measuring the SG

at any point in the cycle you can therefore closely approximate the battery's state of charge at that time.

In practice, a small quantity of electrolyte from each cell in turn is sucked into a bulbed syringe containing a tiny calibrated float. The level at which this floats determines the SG.

Battery state of charge

% of full charge	12V DC	Specific Gravity
100%	12.7	1.265 – 1.275
75%	12.4	1.225 – 1.235
50%	12.2	1.190 – 1.200
25%	12.0	1.155 – 1.165
0%	<11.7	1.120 – 1.130

Continuous monitoring

The simplest device is the humble voltmeter – preferably with an expanded scale spanning the small voltage range significant to lead-acid batteries. But these are rapidly being shouldered aside by electronic instruments of far greater versatility and usefulness.

Specifications and functions vary from brand to brand, but a typical battery monitor will show:

■ A multicolour light bar (Figure 19.1) of some sort giving you the state of charge at a glance.

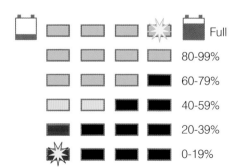

Figure 19.1

■ System voltage
■ System current
■ Percentage of capacity remaining
■ Amp hours consumed or gained
■ Time before recharging is required at current consumption rate

Various values must be entered manually for prediction functions to work, and if these are in error then it's possible for the monitor to get out of sync – perhaps indicating that the battery is running out of capacity when actually it's in good shape. Most monitors have a simple synchronising procedure that will soon put things in order. The precise details should be in its manual!

CAUTION: All batteries deteriorate with time, losing performance as they age. Although their external appearance might look the same, they will never be the same as they were when new. Allowances must be made.

TAKE CARE OF YOUR BATTERIES

Usually tucked out of sight, our unromantic yet crucial battery banks are often neglected. Here are some pointers to keeping them in tip-top condition and prolonging their lives.

■ *Inspect regularly – say, every month. Check the connections for tightness and electrolyte levels where the type allows. Flooded unsealed batteries should be topped up as necessary with distilled or de-ionised water. Never add more sulphuric acid.*

■ *Keep batteries clean. Moisture absorbed into a grimy surface can allow leakage currents. An effective cleaning fluid is a solution of baking soda and water. Then dry thoroughly. Coat the terminals in petroleum jelly (Vaseline®) to keep moisture at bay.*

- *Always try and charge your batteries to full capacity – something many cheap chargers can never achieve. Never leave batteries partially discharged.*

- *It's helpful to keep batteries exercised. Solar panels are ideal for this. They can be safely left unattended and will keep charge levels up in your absence. They will also compensate for any 'parasitic drain' caused by permanently active systems such as alarms, automatic bilge pumps and – ironically – battery monitoring devices.*

- *Be honest with yourself. No matter how good the quality and how assiduously they have been maintained, batteries have finite service lives and will eventually need replacement. One way to see if your batteries are still up to scratch is to conduct a load test.*

Load test

Many batteries have a built in hydrometers (see page 117) seen externally as tiny windows which change colour to indicate charge levels. Useful though these are, they only sample a single cell so are not an indicator of overall condition. There was a time when the terminals of each cell were accessible so their voltage could be checked individually, but this is rarely possible with modern batteries.

These days it's more usual to check the general health of batteries by performing a 'load' or 'drop' test. Here's how:

- *Start with a fully or nearly charged battery which at rest should have a voltage of about 12.6–12.9V depending upon type and age.*

- *Switch on about 10A worth of load and wait for a few minutes. The load could be made up of 5 x 25W navigation lights (about 2A each) or 12 x 10A cabin lights (0.8A each) or a mix of both.*

- *Leave them on for a few minutes then switch them off. Inevitably the battery voltage will have dropped, but the true test is how fast it recovers, so…*

…*wait a few minutes and measure the voltage again. If the battery has bounced back to almost its original level, all is OK and you can put away your wallet. If not, it's pay-out time.*

SMART REGULATORS

For cruising sailors there are significant benefits in boosting their alternators' efficiency by managing their output more intelligently than the standard taper charge arrangements permit.

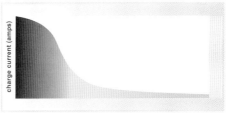

▲ **Taper charging starts strong but diminishes rapidly.**

But be warned. Over-ambitious charge regimes can damage batteries – particularly sealed types where electrolyte losses can never be replaced. It's very important to ensure that whatever regulator you use will not cause undue harm. The most advanced units can be programmed to deal with specific battery types: unsealed lead acid, deep cycle lead acid, sealed gel, and AGM being typical. Some also monitor battery and alternator temperatures, adjusting the charging curves accordingly whilst ensuring that nothing is going amiss.

They divide into two distinct groups:

1. Constant current regulation

These work in conjunction with the inbuilt regulator and are often called 'boosters' – though in some instances this word doesn't do them justice since the most advanced

▲ A 'smart charger' – this one is by Balmar.

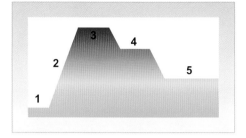

2. Multi-step charging

Top of the line regulators can control the charging regimes even more subtly, thus squeezing the last drop of potential battery-charging capacity out of the process. Again, not all units perform in exactly the same way but the following sequence is typical:

- **Step 1:** Charging is delayed for a short time to allow the engine to warm up.
- **Step 2:** The regulator ramps up the voltage slowly, thus avoiding any sudden loads on the alternator belt.
- **Step 3:** Bulk charge – the most aggressive stage. This will charge the battery to about 80 per cent capacity in the shortest possible time.
- **Step 4:** The regulator ramps down to the 'absorption charge', allowing the battery to accept yet more charge – i.e. to reach as near 100 per cent as possible. This has the additional benefit of reconditioning the battery.
- **Step 5:** With battery fully replenished, the regulator sets about maintaining a 'float charge' to keep the battery topped up and to satisfy any ongoing loads that could drain it. Over an extended period, it will then alternate between absorption and float charges.

will also work as standalone units.

When working in tandem – by far the commonest arrangement – failure of the external controller simply passes the reins back to the original regulator. Understandably, many skippers find this facility reassuring.

Their precise functions vary from unit to unit, with the simplest usually being the least expensive. Overall this type tends to occupy the economy end of the market, but they are still capable of giving valuable service in all but the most demanding circumstances.

WARNING

Most regulators from the US are intended for P-type alternators, with N-type being more common on engines sold in Europe. Check for compatibility. Some manufacturers supply both types. If not, alternators can be converted from one type to another – a relatively simple task but best left to the professionals.

12V TROUBLESHOOTING

Circuits vary in complexity. Some perform very simple roles – supporting a lone bilge pump for instance. Others are more complicated, with a number of related appliances (lighting circuits are for lights, etc.) strung along their length and possibly located some distance apart. Navigation lights and instruments represent obvious examples.

Then there are the mechanical aspects. Does that inert windlass have faulty controls or supply or is it simply seized? The engine fault finding chart on page 138 illustrates the typically inextricable relationship between the invisible world of electrics and the clanking world of mechanical engineering. When things go wrong, recognising the distinction between them will determine what sort of tools you will need to make a repair.

Every cruising boat should carry a multimeter. One of their most useful functions is the testing of electrical 'continuity' – a vital tool in a boat's diagnostic armoury. Indeed, some multimeters have a dedicated continuity setting. When the probes are applied to each end of a conductor – whether a whole circuit or even a single component – a small current from a battery inside the multimeter attempts to pass through it. If the attempt is successful, a beeper sounds, telling us there are no breaks in the circuit.

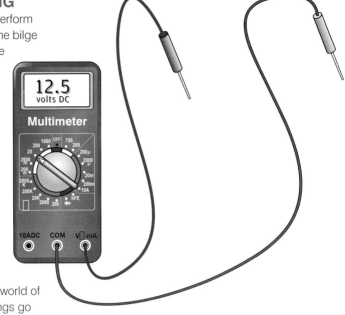

Every cruising boat should carry a multimeter.

But don't despair if your multimeter doesn't have a continuity setting. You can use any of the resistance ranges (Ω) to check. Select a range and the figure '1' should appear in the display. Touch the two probes together and this should be replaced by '00.0' – zero resistance. As you would expect, this most elementary of circuits is complete.

Go to the appendix on page 138 to see how a multimeter could be used in a practical setting.

WARNING

Never attempt to measure resistance or conduct a continuity test on a live circuit. The multimeter relies on its own power source and a powerful external supply will probably blow its fuse. And don't forget to isolate solar panels and wind generators! These are often overlooked.

CHAPTER 20

AC power

Small to mid-size boats can operate perfectly adequately on low voltage systems, but there's a trend – some would say unfortunate – to insist on all the comforts of home while afloat. Such landlubberly devices as microwaves, immersion water heaters, wide-screen TVs and air conditioning are gaining favour – and all demand more power than 12 volts can provide. The only way to satisfy their need is to feed them the sort of fare they would expect ashore: namely an alternating current (AC) of somewhere between 110V–220V.

SHORE POWER

Although relatively few boats regularly use AC at sea (the exceptions often involve computers) the majority take advantage of it when alongside. After all, if the marina operator is thoughtful enough to provide this service, why not accept it? The benefits are many though they are not without risks –

both to human health and the fabric of your boat.

The story starts with the local electricity company supplying 3-phase AC power (typically 415V) to the marina. This is divided into 240V single-phase and distributed to the various pontoons where 3-pin electrical sockets, mounted on pedestals and often metered, are spaced to be accessible to neighbouring boats. The sockets are normally rated at 15A – enough for most purposes but not for very heavy loads such as household-type ovens.

The three conductors that carry the power to the socket are 'live' 'neutral' and 'earth' ('ground' in the US and other places). As can be seen from Figure 20.1 the neutral and earth are linked together ashore (but never on the boat!) and 'earthed' (or 'grounded', it means the same thing) to a pin or plate buried underground. This is to maintain the neutral at 'earth potential' – i.e. zero volts.

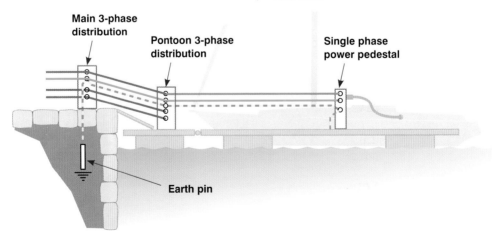

Figure 20.1: Shore power circuit.

The purpose of the earth wire is to provide an escape path for any fault currents to be conducted safely from the boat. In theory, the shore supply's earth should be enough but, regrettably, there are so many links in the chain where resistance can occur that you can't take its integrity for granted. An electrical leak will seek the easiest route to earth, and that could be via your body!

A true story illustrates the point. A young man was preparing a charter yacht for sea. The boat was moored stern-to in the Mediterranean manner. To power the vacuum cleaner and polishers used in the task, an electrical cable had been strung from ashore. Unknown to anyone its insulation had worn through where it crossed the aluminium toe-rail, exposing the live conductor. Everything attached to the toe-rail – including the pushpit – was now energised.

People had been boarding the boat through a transom gate all day without incident but our young man was unlucky. While polishing the pushpit he steadied himself by grabbing the stainless steel steering wheel. This was all the current was waiting for – a path to earth, through the steering linkage and down the rudder stock. Worse still for him, the shock travelled from arm to arm, across the victim's chest, by far the most lethal course. At these voltages a current as low as 60mA can cause ventricular fibrillation and death. Wearing rubber-soled shoes on a GRP deck, he may have been safe if he had not touched the wheel. Then the extension cable might simply have been coiled away and used another day.

Thankfully he survived, but only after vigorous resuscitation and several days in a coma.

Make no mistake: **AC CURRENTS ARE DANGEROUS.**

RESIDUAL CURRENT DEVICES

Our man was doubly unlucky, for there was a bit of kit inside the power pedestal that should have spared him the worst – if not all – effects of the shock had it functioned properly. Such a gadget is known as a 'Residual Current Device' (RCD) and there would almost certainly have been one immediately upstream of the power socket.

RCDs rely on a simple but elegant principle. In a closed circuit the current remains constant throughout its length – in short, what goes in one end has to come out the other. If it doesn't there must be some electrical leakage somewhere. It's the RCD's job to watch out for any differentials and to trip the circuit if one is found.

RCDs are rated at the current differential at which they will operate (30mA being typical for human protection) and the trip speed (30–100msecs of 'break time'). They are sometimes combined with overload protection circuit breakers, whereupon they become known as RCBOs.

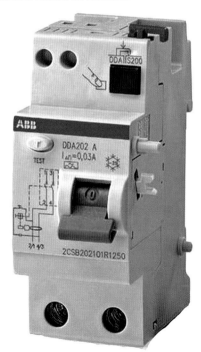

▲ **A typical Residual Current Device (RCD).**

REVERSE POLARITY

It's an astonishing fact that the polarity of shore power cannot be relied upon. Since AC appliances don't care about polarity, operating contentedly regardless of which cables are live or neutral, many marinas feel free to adopt slapdash standards.

The results can be very dangerous. Switches, fuses and single-pole CBs should always be in the live side of a circuit – and of course wouldn't be if the neutral was live instead. Many boats have a polarity test facility built into their AC panels. An inexpensive alternative is a portable plug-type tester (left) that will also reveal any earth or neutral faults.

Some AC panels have switches that will correct reverse polarity. If not, a simple remedy is to swap the live and neutral connections at the plug.

Shore supply polarity can be corrected by introducing a short cross-wired section into the shore power cable.

AC DISTRIBUTION

The simplest, and perhaps most familiar, use of AC involves hooking an extension cord into the pontoon to allow a charger to feed the various battery banks. Thereafter the boat runs entirely on its DC system.

Simple it may be, with few opportunities for faults, but some sensible precautions should still be taken to make it as safe as possible. The basic arrangement is shown in Figure 20.2 – portable, inexpensive but far from ideal.

Figure 20.3 shows a rather more elaborate installation where the AC is used 'raw' to power on-board appliances. Note that the live input is protected by an RCBO – thereby guarding against both overload and current leakage – and that there's a 'polarity'

Figure 20.2: Although not ideal, a portable RCD will make an extension cord safer.

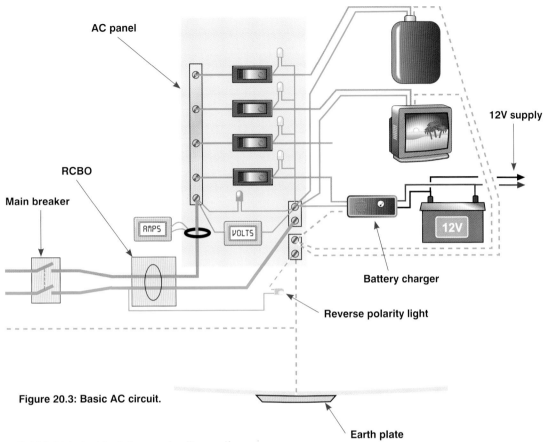

AC panel

RCBO

Main breaker

AMPS

VOLTS

12V supply

12V

Battery charger

Reverse polarity light

Figure 20.3: Basic AC circuit.

Earth plate

light (which, incidentally, remains lit even if the RCBO trips) to check that the live and neutral are connected properly. Each of the various branches also has its own RCD.

This still remains a relatively elementary set-up, but it does serve to illustrate the basic principles. The reality is that, as average boat sizes increase and demands for on-board comfort gather pace, AC systems are becoming more and more complicated. Indeed, in the very largest yachts, AC might take over the central role entirely. For obvious reasons this is not a subject that impacts on many of us.

USEFUL READING

For comprehensive advice on boat electrics, read the *RYA Electrics Handbook* (G67).

APPENDIX 1

Pair painting with Awlgrip® two-part polyurethane

Throughout this book I have avoided recommending specific products but when it comes to hand painting (as opposed to spray painting) two-part polyurethanes there has to be an exception. Whereas other paint manufacturers employ special thinners to make hand painting possible, Awlgrip use a dedicated hardener to make their product more amenable. The end effects can be startlingly good. However, the potential for getting it horribly wrong remains significant so don't attempt to do this yourself if you're in any doubt about your abilities.

In any kind of painting, preparation is the key so let's start there and take it step by step, starting with the weathered gelcoat.

1: It's absolutely essential that all traces of any previous paintwork be removed, including cove lines, sign writing etc. Also polishes – particularly those heavily loaded with silicone such as many automotive types. Start by washing the surface with a detergent, then fill any major gouges, pinholes or areas of crazing (the latter might require grinding out and repair) with an epoxy filler. Allow the filler to cure.

2: Using either a random orbit or orbital sander, abrade the surface with 120 grit abrasive paper, using light pressure and ensuring that the sander stays flat – i.e. that an edge doesn't dig in to create a gouge. Be very thorough with this task. There should be no even remotely shiny areas when you have finished.

3: Mask off all areas that won't be painted.

The waterline and rub rails come to mind. If working outdoors, be mindful of the fact that masking tape can 'bake on' in sunlight making it very difficult to remove. Use a good-quality tape that will stand a bit of weathering.

4: It's time to apply the primer. This will seal any porosity in the surface of the gelcoat. Awlgrip recommend their 545 but many painters elect to use other products. These are two-part products which must be mixed in accordance with the manufacturer's instructing, being meticulous with the proportions. Don't be tempted to add more hardener 'just to be on the safe side' to any of these products. The hardener is not a catalyst. The cure of epoxies and polyurethanes involves a co-activation process where the two parts combine to produce the finished resin.

Apply the primer with a paint roller. Ideally the roller should be of sponge, but these can be subject to solvent attack and can fall apart in minutes. If using a pile-type roller, buy the best you can.

Wear activated carbon masks and solvent-resistant gloves. The solvents are harmful. Use a combination of vertical followed by horizontal strokes. Allow to dry in accordance with directions – overnight being typical. Regard the rollers as disposable. Discard after every coat.

5: Once the first primer coat is hard, sand it back with 220 grit abrasive, then repeat step 4 as many times (usually two or three) as is necessary to produce an absolutely fair surface, ensuring that every coat is applied

Note the plastic cup in the brush painter's hand used for scraping excess paint from the bristles.

possible to paint one side of a boat in the morning and the other in the afternoon, once the sun has moved over.

We touched on the pair painting (also known as roll-and-tip) technique back on page 33. It involves one person applying the paint with vertical strokes of a roller and his partner 'laying it off' with the tip of a good-quality natural-fibre brush. The brush is used in horizontal strokes working in towards the 'wet edge' – i.e. the preceding section that's just been painted. Work methodically in vertical sections no more than 50cm or so wide.

If you look at the photo left you will see the secret weapon in the brush painter's left hand. It's actually a yoghurt cup or similar which is used to remove the overload of paint that will inevitably build up in the brush's bristles. The amount of paint you apply is very much a matter of judgement but the good news is that practice makes perfect and you will learn with each successive coat.

You will need a minimum of two coats, lightly 'de-nibbing' with 400 grit wet-or-dry (used wet) between coats. If allowed to cure for more than 24 hours you must abrade more thoroughly. If you want a really deep shine you may need three or four coats and, considering the work you have already put in, it is worth taking the trouble. Obviously, you don't abrade the finished coat.

to a dry and dust-free surface. Sticky cloths known as 'tack-rags' are useful for removing the last vestiges of dust.

The final primer coat should be sanded back by hand using 400 grit wet-or-dry used wet.

6: Now for the first of the Awlgrip two-part (actually three if you include the thinner) polyurethane finish coats, remembering to use the combination specially formulated for hand painting (base resin plus H3002 converter, 2/1 by volume). Again, mix and thin as instructed. Allow the mixed paint to stand for 15 minutes to allow 'induction' and for air bubbles to come to the surface. If working outside choose a dry day, preferably without direct sunlight. Depending on orientation, it's sometimes

---

WARNING: The various chemicals used in two-part polyurethanes are potentially harmful and can sometimes cause quite severe allergic reactions. Read the manufacturer's safety instructions and follow them to the letter.

APPENDIX 2

Banishing the blisters: osmosis treatment

MAKE NO MISTAKE: There is no simple cure to a blistered hull

Once water has been absorbed into the laminate the possibility of blisters developing will always exist. Simply allowing a hull to 'dry' naturally and then slapping on a couple of token coats of epoxy resin might create the illusion of a permanent cure but will be far from it. As covered back in Chapter 3 you should either live with the problem (which will probably only advance very slowly) or bite the bullet and invest in radical treatment.

But just how radical? It was once thought sufficient simply to grit blast the hull to knock out the rash of blisters, allow the hull to dry (perhaps over the winter lay-up period with the drying process being monitored by a surveyor) before applying the epoxy the following spring. Lots of time and money has been sacrificed in what is almost always a vain endeavour. Eventual failure of such a treatment is almost guaranteed.

The problem is that, although the moisture level of the laminate might have fallen, most of the contaminants it contains

▲ **Ideally, you should have a surveyor check the laminate's moisture levels.**

▲ Gelcoat peeling will remove most of the osmotic damage.

remain. It will only be a matter of time before the problem returns and your well-intentioned plans will be as nought.

Consider the cost

When debating whether to treat a boat or not, it's helpful to think about the costs relative to the boat's value. Let's take an elderly 25-footer. A full osmosis repair as described below could well exceed the value of the boat. The project might be justifiable as a labour of love, but in purely monetary terms it makes no sense whatsoever. The owner will probably decide to live with the problem, reassuring himself that it will only advance slowly.

By contrast let's assume a 50-footer. In doubling the size of the boat, the area to be treated will increase approximately by the square, meaning that the treatment costs will have risen about fourfold. However the value of the larger boat could easily be twenty times that of the smaller one, making the repair a far more acceptable proposition.

Preparing the hull

The only certain cure is to remove the gelcoat entirely, exposing the laminate so it can be cleaned and dried. The most effective implement for removing gelcoat is a specialised electric planer with super-hard tungsten carbide blades. Since such a tool is capable of inflicting serious damage, this is definitely a job best entrusted to a professional.

Ideally, all underwater skin fittings should be removed but awkwardness of access (the accursed thoughtlessness of some boatbuilders to consider anything but their own convenience!) can make this very difficult, if not impossible.

Once peeled, the exposed laminate should be lightly grit-blasted (a service often offered by the person that planed the hull). Next, it should be washed, possibly with a high-pressure water jet or, better still, steam cleaned using a heavyweight industrial cleaner, available from many tool hire companies. This will remove most of the contaminants.

Next, allow the hull to dry. For the DIYer this is usually over the winter lay-up period. Have this monitored periodically by a local surveyor who will advise when the hull is ready for the restorative work to start. You might also seek his advice on one other often overlooked but extremely important issue. Namely…

How thick is the laminate?

Gelcoat peeling is a fairly brutal process. Along with the gelcoat, it's almost inevitable that some of the glassfibre reinforcements will be removed. The structural loss may be insignificant in a heavily built boat but this may not be the case for one of light construction – increasingly common in these cost-conscious days.

If it is thought that some significant structural impairment has occurred, it will be necessary to sheath the underwater surfaces using light bi-axial rovings (about 450gm/m^2) and epoxy resin. Some experts advise using twill weave glass cloth because it 'drapes' well but this will be very awkward to work when working overhead. Again, at least consider professional assistance – the potential for disaster is high!

While the newly sheathed areas are still tacky they should be covered with 'peel-ply' – a disposable protective cloth that seals the surface from the air (thereby preventing the occurrence of unwanted 'amine waxing' which can occur if it's cool and damp) and also imparts a texture to the cured surface that will help subsequent layers adhere. An alternative is to apply a coat of an epoxy primer (such as Gelshield 200®) that can be overcoated as long as six months later without problem. Note that with both options the work MUST be done before the sheathing resin hardens.

Sealing and fairing

The final stage of the work is to apply further coats of epoxy – a minimum of five if using a brush and/or roller. These sealing coats are usually supplied in two contrasting colours which you should use alternately to ensure you get an even coverage. Hopefully, you won't have to do too much fairing but special epoxy paste products that can be trowelled on are available.

Although the professionals often use products from different sources – perhaps the resin from one manufacturer, fillers from another – the DIYer would be advised to stick with one product range where compatibility is guaranteed.

And **FOLLOW THE MANUFACTURER'S INSTRUCTIONS.** Detailed data sheets are available for all brands and you will find suppliers generally very helpful with further advice. When they say a product should not be used below, say, 5ºC they mean it. Ditto the maximum and minimum overcoat times, which will vary with the ambient temperature.

To illustrate the importance of the previous paragraph, please let me relate a true story. A good friend (and Oxford don) was applying protective coats of epoxy to his boat's hull. He rolled on the first coat, inspected it closely, even touched it with a fingertip. Then, being far cleverer than the chemists who formulated the resin, he decided that the minimum overcoat time was a fiction. Around lunchtime he rolled up at the yacht club bar crowing that two days' work had been completed in just a single morning. Why, if the weather held he would get the whole job done over the weekend.

Unfortunately not. Returning to admire his work before going home, he was astonished to find his boat surrounded by a ring of amused bystanders. For his shiny new epoxy now hung in tendrils, some reaching the ground to pool on the concrete. What had happened was this. Epoxies are 'exothermic' – meaning they generate heat as they cure. And, as the resin warms, its viscosity reduces – in this case to the point where the first coat simply became too liquid to support the subsequent one.

So, to repeat:
FOLLOW THE MANUFACTURER'S INSTRUCTIONS!

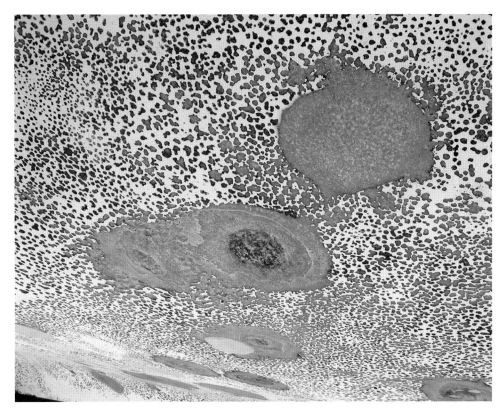

No, the photograph on this page isn't the surface of some far-off planet; it shows the surface of a hull, badly afflicted with osmotic blistering. It also shows why grit-blasting as the first pre-treatment is a largely futile exercise. Firstly, so much of the gelcoat has been removed that it would have been better to have planed it all away in the first place. Secondly, despite the comprehensive damage, there can be no guarantee that there are no blisters still lurking under what little gelcoat remains.

For the owner of this boat, the news got worse. Once the grit-blasting had been completed, it became apparent that certain patches of the hull were much damper than the rest. More accurately, water was weeping from the surface. In order to investigate further, these areas were ground back. As can be seen in the crater just left of centre, a number of the glass laminates were separating – a condition aptly known as delamination. The inescapable truth is

that this hull was in very poor condition – probably irreparable.

This is one of the worst cases this author has ever seen – exceptional by any standards. I learned that the boat had spent many years in the Mediterranean. As we noted back on page 18, warm waters are more invasive than cold, and the boats that ply them generally spend more time afloat. And there can be other causal factors – mainly down to shoddy working practices. The resins could have been out of date, the catalyst proportions incorrect, or maybe there had been poor workplace temperature control – insufficient temperature being the usual villain. Any of those may have inhibited the cure, resulting in a sub-standard laminate.

So the message is don't panic! Where GRP laminating is concerned, both the materials and working practices have improved vastly over the years. Very, very few boat owners – hopefully none – will have to face such shocking news today.

APPENDIX 3

Tuning your rig

Once we have the mast in the boat we can set about the tuning of the rigging. For tools you will need:

■ Adjustable spanners – one to hold the top of the rigging screw while the barrel is rotated, and another to fit the barrel. Always use quality spanners and adjusters which are in good condition. Rusty tools will contaminate the rigging, probably leaving a rust residue.
■ A steel rule (about 30cm long) to ensure that the rigging screws are all tensioned equally.
■ A bosun's chair (see page 134) to ascend the mast.
From there on, the sequence goes like this:

1: Make sure your mast rake is correct then tighten the backstay. The amount of rake is specified by the designer and, if possible, should be taken off the sailplan.

2: Now tighten the cap shrouds, ensuring that the rigging screw threads are equal inside the rigging screw and on both sides of the boat.

3: It's a good idea at this point to check that the masthead is on the centreline. Ideally this should have been done when the mast was on the ground by ensuring that the cap shrouds were exactly the same length. If that was the case it's reasonable to

assume that once the mast is standing, the masthead must be on the centreline if the cap shrouds are adjusted equally.

4: The next task is to make sure the mast is 'in column'. Peer up the mainsail track and adjust the lower shrouds to take out any lateral deviations. As for the fore-and-aft alignment, masts usually have what's known as 'pre-bend', an adjustment made to suit mainsail shape – see page 65. Again, this should be specified by the designer but somewhere around 25 per cent of the fore-and-aft dimension on the mast section should be about right. Use the forward lower shrouds, if there are any, or the baby stay if there are not.
On swept spreader rigs the pre-bend is induced by the forward thrust of the spreaders and isn't quite so straightforward to get right. But we will deal with this in the section that follows.

Cap shrouds

Forestay

Backstay

Lower shrouds

5: Leave the final tuning until you are sailing. Put the boat on a close-hauled course sailing to windward in flat water and a fairish breeze. Look up the mast to see how straight it is both fore-and-aft and athwartships. If, say, the top of the mast falls away to leeward, you will

know that the windward cap shroud needs to be tightened. If the middle of the mast falls away it will require the lowers to be tightened. See how it looks on both tacks.

6: Resist the temptation to make adjustments at sea. Better by far to note what needs to be done and complete these tasks back in your berth where they can be done precisely. Then check the tuning again the next time you go out.

Tuning single swept-spreader rigs

When adjusting masts with swept spreaders, it's important to understand how their geometry works. With this type of rig the spreaders induce a forward force into the mast, so affect the mast's shape both from side-to-side and fore-and-aft. This makes them a little more time-consuming to tune.

1: Begin by adjusting the forestay to get the correct mast rake.

2: Tighten the backstay quite firmly.

3: Next, tension the cap shrouds ensuring as for non-swept spreaders that they are the same on both sides. Indeed, from now on, any further adjustments must be identical on both sides.

4: If the mast has both forward and aft lower shrouds, tension the forward ones first. Then look up the after side of the mast to make sure the track is straight and, therefore, that

the mast is 'in column'. There should also be some pre-bend.

5: Now it's time to adjust the aft lowers, but be careful not to over-tension them since this will pull the pre-bend out of the mast.

Forestay

6: Lastly, check the forestay tension by hand – making sure there's no more than a little sag in the roller reefing – before going aft and tightening the backstay.

Backstay

Lower shrouds

Cap shrouds

7: Again, make the final checks under sail, making notes of any adjustments that might be necessary. Remember that the mast must remain in column on both tacks. If the top of the mast falls away to leeward, the cap shrouds should be tightened; if the middle falls away, the aft lowers should be tightened.

Multi-spreader swept fractional rigs

These are tuned in much the same way as for single-spreader rigs but you may need a bosun's chair to adjust the intermediate shrouds.

Lower and intermediate shrouds control the athwartships alignment of the mast.

USING A BOSUN'S CHAIR

Ascending a mast is something most sailors will need to do some day. Often this is a task which is completed rather light-heartedly but the reality is that it's a high-risk operation which – should it go wrong – could result in serious injury, at worst even a fatality.

Early bosun's chairs were simply short planks of wood, rigged with rope strops to provide the attachments. They were notoriously easy to fall out of. By contrast, modern chairs are made of strong synthetic fabric and wrap around the hips of the climber, with straps between the legs and around the waist. The seat itself is usually stiffened for added comfort. Properly adjusted, the chair will hold the climber securely in place, allowing him (or her) to work with both hands without fear of being dislodged. Most chairs come complete with a variety of pockets to carry tools and other necessary objects.

There are also various proprietary devices designed to allow someone to climb a mast unaided but these fall outside the scope of this book. Here we're assuming at least one other assistant and what can be considered the 'conventional' way of getting a crew member aloft.

Up the stick...

The climber will be pulled up the mast on a halyard, with another halyard used as a safety backup. For the primary line the main halyard is usually the obvious choice, because:

■ It passes through the masthead which means that security isn't reliant on the strength of the sheave.

■ It usually leads comfortably to a powerful winch.

Basic points:

1. The primary line should be tied to the chair's attachment point with a bowline. Never rely on a shackle or snapshackle – though, if these can be attached as well they will provide additional security.

2. The backup line is usually the spinnaker halyard and, in this case, it's sometimes better to use its (almost invariable) snapshackle, since the climber may need to detach and then reattach it in order to negotiate the spreaders.

3. With this arrangement, you need at least two crew on deck to handle the halyards (plus one more to tail the main halyard if the winch isn't self-tailing). The bulk of the work lies with the main halyard winchman, with the other taking up the slack and keeping an eye on what's going on up the mast. Some people like both winchers to share the load, but this can lead to confusion.

■ Note that self-tailers should only be used in self-tailing mode if there are also rope clutches as backups.

GOLDEN RULES

RULE 1: While he's actually winching, the principal winchman should keep his eyes on the winch, not the climber. This will avoid the chance of any riding turns or other foul-ups.

RULE 2: If the halyard winches are on the mast, send the tools up in a bucket once the climber is in place. To have, say, a cordless drill fall from the bosun's chair onto the wincher standing below could be bad news for everyone concerned – not least for the climber who could follow it to the deck if said wincher became distracted.

RULE 3: Once the halyards are secured, stand clear of the mast while work is in progress.
   This method presumes a crew of three but many cruising crews consist of sailing couples, in which circumstances it would be dangerous for a single wincher to be operating two winches. So, an alternative to the backup line is for the climber to use a mountaineering 'ascender' (a type of jamming cleat) attached to the chair via a short rope strop and run up a spare halyard which has been set up fairly tight by tensioning it with a winch. Again, the spinnaker halyard is a strong candidate for this role.

... and down again.

With gravity now on your side, life becomes less strenuous for the winchers, but don't allow the feeling of relative ease relax your concentration.

RULE 4: Again, as you lower the climber, the wincher's eyes should be on the drum, not up the mast. Riding turns are more common when easing than when hauling. And...

RULE 5: The winchers must ease the halyards hand-over-hand, instead of allowing the rope to slip through their fingers. This is in case something sharp – a piece of glass or wire, for instance – has become caught in the rope, the sudden pain of which might cause a startled wincher to release his grip.

APPENDIX 4

Engine start circuit test

We have all been there: you turn the engine start key and very little happens. There was a time when many smaller marine engines could be started by hand but this is rarely the case these days.

Fortunately, it's a fairly simple matter to test the circuit to try and identify the fault. All you need is a multimeter set to measure 20VDC (volts DC). Before you start you should extend the negative (–) lead and connect one end to the engine block or some other convenient earth. This will allow you to wander about with the meter in hand.

First check that the main isolating switch is switched 'ON', then proceed as follows, starting at the battery:

■ Measure the battery voltage between the battery posts (1). The voltage should be at least 12V.
ACTION: *Charge battery if necessary.*

■ Now shift the probes to the terminals (2) that connect the cables to the posts. If the voltage is noticeably lower, one or both of the connections must be suspect.
ACTION: *Remove terminals, clean all connecting surfaces and reassemble. At*

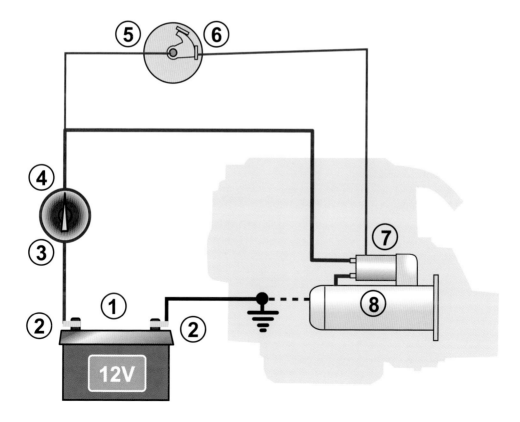

this time also check the negative (ground) connection to the engine block. Vibration could have loosened it.

■ Check the voltage first at (3) then on the other side of the isolation/selector switch, which of course must be 'ON', at (4). There should be very little difference. A voltage drop would signal a defective switch or poor connections.
ACTION: *Remake connections. If the problem persists replace the switch.*

■ Check the voltage at (5). If OK…

■ …move the probe to the output (solenoid) side of the starter switch or button (6) and operate switch. The full voltage should be apparent. Again, if it isn't, this is likely to be a problem with either the connections or the switch. Key-type switches are notoriously fallible so expect the worst.
ACTION: *These are sealed units with no internal access. Replacement is the only option.*

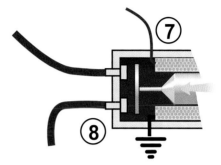

■ Check voltage at (7). If OK …

■ …Turn the switch 'ON' again and check the voltage at (8). If the solenoid (which acts as a switch to summon up the large current needed by the starter motor) is working properly this should show a healthy voltage. If not, the problem lies inside the relay. Either the solenoid coil is malfunctioning or the heavy-duty contact points have been eroded away.
ACTION: *You could check the coil by running a continuity test on it (remember to switch the power 'OFF'). It should show a low resistance. But this is fairly academic, since it's now time to call in the professionals. Except there is one last possibility…*

■ Make sure that the starter motor unit is securely mounted. The negative return needed to complete the circuit is via the metal casing. If the motor has vibrated loose, the connection may not be good enough.

APPENDIX 5

Fault finding charts

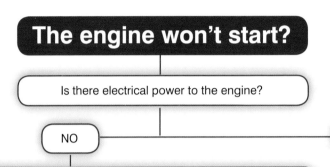

The engine won't start?

Is there electrical power to the engine?

NO   YES

1) Is the battery isolation switch 'On'?

2) Check for blown fuse or tripped circuit breaker

3) Is the battery totally discharged?

4) Are the battery terminal leads connected?

5) Is the battery earth lead to the engine block connected and secure?

1) This is a common but surprisingly easy mistake to make. The usual arrangement is to have a single switch in the positive side of the circuit, but many European boats also isolate the negative side. Both must be switched on for the engine to start.

2) Engine control fuses aren't always easy to find. There may be a small fuse box mounted on the engine block somewhere or – a ridiculous practice on some engines – it could even be wound in beneath the engine wiring loom insulation! You may have to consult the service manual.

3) A battery's voltage doesn't have to be zero for it to be useless. A fully charged 12V battery at rest will show around 12.8V. By the time that reading drops to 10.5V it's effectively 100 per cent flat. If your power management system includes a voltmeter or bar graph-type state-of-charge indicator, monitoring the battery condition is very straightforward. If not, you will have to resort to a hydrometer or portable multimeter.

4) Engine starting creates high electrical demands. Any voltage drop due to corroded or loose connections can result in total failure. Check that there's no corrosion and that the terminal clamps are tight on the posts.

5) The same goes for the cable that goes from the battery negative to the engine block. Vibration can easily loosen the connection, so make sure it's clean and nip up the securing bolt.

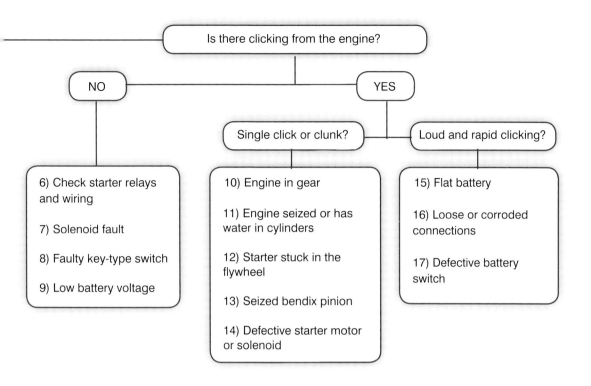

Is there clicking from the engine?

NO

YES

Single click or clunk?

Loud and rapid clicking?

6) Check starter relays and wiring

7) Solenoid fault

8) Faulty key-type switch

9) Low battery voltage

10) Engine in gear

11) Engine seized or has water in cylinders

12) Starter stuck in the flywheel

13) Seized bendix pinion

14) Defective starter motor or solenoid

15) Flat battery

16) Loose or corroded connections

17) Defective battery switch

6) Starter solenoids can draw quite a lot of power. To avoid running heavy cables from the starting switch to the solenoid, a secondary switch known as a 'relay' is often used. Turning the ignition key activates the relay which, in turn, switches on the power to operate the solenoid. Relays are unserviceable items. If defective they should be replaced.

7) Solenoids sometimes get stuck. They can often be freed by tapping them lightly with the power on. Lightly, mind: **DON'T CLOUT IT HARD WITH A HAMMER!**

8) Key-type switches are notoriously prone to faults. Push-button ones are much more reliable. The switch can be bypassed by connecting across the solenoid terminals.

9) If your cabin lights dim when you operate the starting switch, you can be sure that the batteries are at a low state of charge. Try switching off all other appliances so the starter motor can have what little power is left.

10) Most engines will start in gear but if the prop is heavily fouled there may be too much resistance.

11) If the water has only been in the engine a short time, you can act to prevent expensive damage. If it has seized, you are almost certainly facing a complete overhaul.

12, 13 & 14) The starter motor should be removed so it can be freed up or sent away for repair.

15) If the engine can't be hand-started, there's nothing for it but to find some other means of charging the battery.

16) Clean and tighten as required.

17) Bypass or replace.

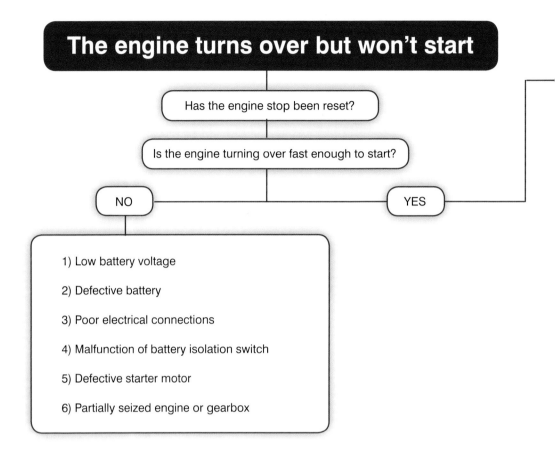

The engine turns over but won't start

Has the engine stop been reset?

Is the engine turning over fast enough to start?

NO

YES

1) Low battery voltage

2) Defective battery

3) Poor electrical connections

4) Malfunction of battery isolation switch

5) Defective starter motor

6) Partially seized engine or gearbox

1, 2 & 3) When it comes to engine starting, cranking speed is of the essence. And, since the rotation is usually gained by electrical power, look towards the most obvious causes before suspecting anything more dramatic. If your batteries have deteriorated to the point where they will no longer hold their charge, there's no solution other than replacement. However, there are a couple of tricks that might get you out of trouble. If there are decompression levers on your engine, open them until the speed mounts, then drop them down.

4) Isolating switches are fairly robust by nature, but wear and sparking can damage their internal contacts, thereby increasing resistance. Replacement is the only permanent cure but a temporary fix can be achieved by taking the switch out of the circuit entirely. The easiest way of doing this is to connect both cable terminals to the same connector post on the back of the switch.

5) The field windings could be breaking down or the bearings could be worn or partially seized. If the motor gets very hot to the touch, this is a sure sign that it's drawing lots of current and ailing seriously. It should be reconditioned or replaced.

6) Time for an overhaul.

7) Since tanks usually run dry while the engine is running, it would be very odd indeed if you suddenly found it empty. Check that a leak hasn't dumped the fuel into the bilge. And remember: whatever the cause, once everything is shipshape again the system will require bleeding before you can run the engine. See page 93.

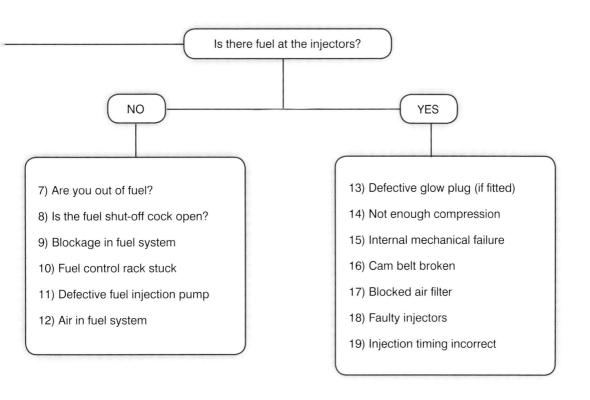

Is there fuel at the injectors?

NO

YES

7) Are you out of fuel?

8) Is the fuel shut-off cock open?

9) Blockage in fuel system

10) Fuel control rack stuck

11) Defective fuel injection pump

12) Air in fuel system

13) Defective glow plug (if fitted)

14) Not enough compression

15) Internal mechanical failure

16) Cam belt broken

17) Blocked air filter

18) Faulty injectors

19) Injection timing incorrect

8) An easy oversight. You are not alone!

9) The causes of blockage can be many. First, check the pre-filter to see if there's anything in the sediment bowl. Then act accordingly.

10 & 11) This is dragon country and none but the most expert should venture inside. Time to get help.

12) Bleed the engine. See page 93.

13) The engine is too cold. You may have better luck at a warmer time of day or perhaps you can warm the engine gently by other means – a hot water bottle, for instance.

14) Take off the air filter and aim a couple of squirts of oil as deep into the inlet manifold

as possible. The objective is to allow the oil to run down the cylinder walls – it will help seal the piston rings. Be careful not to overdo it. Oil is incompressible and excessive amounts could damage the engine. As soon as the engine fires, replace the air filter. This, of course, is only a short-term measure. The problem is one of general wear and tear and the need for an overhaul is imminent.

15 & 16) Time to call an engineer.

17) Replace or clean.

18) Replace or send away for servicing.

19) Consult your engine manual. This can be quite a simple job on some engines. If in doubt, call in an engineer.

APPENDIX 6

Tools and spares

It seems an essential truth that no matter how many tools and spares you carry you will eventually come across a problem that calls for something you don't have. However, it makes sense to at least attempt to anticipate what might be needed and then to stow it somewhere accessible. Another essential truth is that when you need a tool or spare you often need it in a hurry. The time to start searching lockers for, say, an engine drive belt is not when it parts as you enter a marina.

And, when it comes to tools, buy the best you can afford. The inexperienced mechanic needs all the help he or she can get and certainly can do without the deficiencies of cheap and nasty gear. Although the list is potentially endless, let's make a typical selection…

Mechanical toolkit

■ **A full workshop manual for the engine.** The nursery version that comes with the engine is rarely sufficient. Even if you call in a professional mechanic, having detailed information to hand will be very useful.

■ **Spanners or wrenches.** 7mm to 24mm AF (across flats) in metric sizes; 1/4in to 1in in imperial. Although most European and Far Eastern gear uses metric-sized fastenings, the Americans still cling to the older, imperial measurements. Combination spanners have open jaws at one end and 'rings' on the other. It's not uncommon to find both on a boat. Spanners with open jaws at both ends are almost invariably sized differently –

i.e. 12mm and 14mm. This should mean that you can carry half the number of spanners but remember that you often need a spanner at both ends of a bolt – one to undo the nut and another to stop the bolt from turning.

■ **Adjustable spanner.** The professionals might wince but these are undeniably useful – particularly in larger sizes. Carry two – one that opens wider than your largest spanner and a smaller one for general use.

■ **Socket set.** 3/8in drive is the most versatile but the smaller 1/4in drive is also useful.

■ **Strap wrench.** For removing filter cartridges.

■ **Screwdrivers.** A selection, comprehensive in size and both flat bladed and cross-point. The short 'dumpy' types are also handy.

■ **Pliers.** Conventional and needle-nosed. Also useful are what are known as 'water pump pliers' or 'crescent wrenches'.

■ **Vice grips** (Mole wrench being typical).

■ **Hacksaw** and spare blades.

■ **Files.** Round and flat.

■ **Craft knife.**

■ **Set of Allen keys.** Both metric and imperial.

■ **Hammer.** Lightish in weight and of the 'ball peen' type.

■ **Lump (club) hammer.**

■ **Feeler gauges.**

■ **Punches.** Parallel (straight) for driving out cotter pins and the like.

■ **Grease gun and oilcan.**

■ **Large magnet.** For retrieving tools from bilge (or overboard).

■ **Tape measure.**

■ **Rechargeable drill and bits.** Although not essential, this is a useful luxury to have on board.

Electrical toolkit

■ **Multimeter.** Digital type preferably.

■ **Polarity tester.** For testing mains voltage shore-power polarity – often incorrect in marinas abroad.

■ **Crimping tool** and selection of crimp-type connectors and terminals.

■ **Wire stripper.**

■ **Small screwdrivers.**

■ **Side cutter.**

■ **Butane soldering iron.**

■ **Insulating tape.**

■ **Self-amalgamating tape.**

■ **Heat shrink tape.**

■ **Hydrometer** (if you have conventional flooded lead-acid batteries).

Rigging Bag

■ **Splicing fids.** For splicing braidline.

■ **Marlin spike.**

■ **Rigger's knife.**

■ **Sailmakers' palm** and an assortment of needles.

■ **Assorted whipping twines.**

■ **Scissors.**

■ **Beeswax.**

■ **Monel® seizing wire.**

Spares

■ **Oil for engine and gearbox.** Check if the gearbox uses automatic transmission fluid (ATF).

■ **Oil filter.**

■ **Fuel filter.** Both pre-filter and fine filter.

■ **Air cleaner element.** If there is one.

■ **Crankcase breather element.** If there is one.

■ **Pump impellers.** The most important being the raw water cooling pump.

■ **Belts.** At least one spare for each.

■ **Hoses.**

■ **Gasket material and sealant.**

■ **Grease** for any stern gland that uses it.

■ **Engine anodes.**

■ **Sparkplugs.** For outboard motors.

APPENDIX 7

Soft furnishing – let no stain remain

Boats can be messy. That's the long and short of it. Indeed, you would be hard-pressed to imagine a conveyance more wickedly contrived to scatter foodstuffs and beverages far and wide. Most sailors have known what it is to have scalding coffee or soup poured over them. And those unlucky enough to have experienced a knockdown will tell you what joy it is to have a whole table-load of food slide towards you, at least some of it destined for your lap.

Well, laps are easily cleaned. It's the collateral staining to carpets and upholstery where the greatest challenge lies. How to deal with the crisis calls for good sense, a bit of chemistry and some household cleaning potions you should carry on your boat. These are:

- Washing soda crystals – (alkaline). Use diluted in water roughly in the proportions of one teaspoon per cup or about one cup per bucket.
- Ammonia (an even stronger alkali). Again diluted, two tablespoons per litre.
- White vinegar (acidic). Two tablespoons per litre.
- Spot remover (dry cleaning solvent).
- Paper towels.

Resist the temptation to increase the concentrations. It's not necessary and could cause damage.

Also, notice that there is nothing in the list that makes suds. No carpet shampoo or anything like that. The problem with sudsy cleaners is that they leave residues in the fabric. If you think of how much rinsing it takes to remove suds from a sponge, you will understand why this is the case. And these residues are slightly sticky and will attract yet more dirt in the future.

Now let's move on to the chemistry. The majority of stains are acidic. These include fruit juices, wine, most vegetables, meat, culinary sauces, and all bodily fluids. Acidic stains are best dealt with by applying alkaline cleaners.

Tea and coffee on the other hand are alkaline, and with these the remedies should be acidic – our white vinegar to be specific.

When there's a spill your first reaction should be DON'T PANIC! It's all too easy to make matters worse by doing the wrong thing. Curse a little by all means but suppress the urge to do anything rash.

Liquid spills

- Mop up large quantities of the liquid with a folded towel. Press down or stand on the towel if you can.
- Scrape up any solids, semi-solids or grease with a knife or spoon.
- Be careful you don't spread the spill wider. Work from the outside to the inside of the area.
- Apply clean warm water or the washing soda solution.
- Finally, rinse with clean water and spread paper towels over the damp patch to absorb excess moisture.

Semi-solid or greasy spills

- Use a knife or spoon to scrape up as much of the mess as possible.
- Then use the washing soda solution to remove what else remains. Obstinate grease spots may need dry cleaning solvent.
- Rinse and dry as before.

After treating your stains, it's wise to restore the acid/alkali balance so it is neither one thing nor the other (pH = 7). This means an application of, say, ammonia, should be neutralised with a little vinegar, and vice-versa.

So much for generalities. The tables advise how to deal with specific problems:

TYPE OF STAIN	CLEANING SEQUENCE
Asphalt	1. Solvent
Butter, margarine	2. Blot
Cooking oil	3. Washing soda
Sun cream	4. Blot
Gravy and other sauces	5. Water
Hair oil	6. Blot
Hand lotion	
Ink (ball point)	
Ink (felt tip marker)	
Lard	
Linseed or tung oil	
Machine oil	
Mascara	
Salad dressing	
Tar or soot	
Cheese	1. Washing soda
Chocolate	2. Blot
Egg	3. Ammonia
Excrement	4. Blot
Soil	5. Detergent
Ice cream	6. Blot
Ketchup	7. Water
Mayonnaise	8. Blot
Milk	
Soy sauce	
Starch	
Toothpaste	
Beer	1. Washing soda
Berries	2. Blot
Coffee	3. Vinegar
Fruit juice	4. Washing soda
Mixed drinks	5. Blot
Soft drinks	6. Water
Sweets	7. Blot
Tea	
Wine	
Ink (permanent)	
Vomit	1. Washing soda
	2. Blot
	3. Ammonia
	4. Blot
	5. White vinegar
	6. Blot
	7. Water
	8. Blot

TYPE OF STAIN	CLEANING SEQUENCE
Ink (fountain pen)	1. Detergent
	2. Blot
	3. White vinegar
	4. Blot
	5. Ammonia
	6. Blot
	7. Water
	8. Blot
Urine	1. Blot
	2. Water
	3. Blot
	4. Ammonia
	5. Washing soda
	6. Blot
	7. Water
	8. Blot
Blood	Use cold ingredients
	1. Washing soda
	2. Blot
	3. Vinegar
	4. Blot
	5. Ammonia
	6. Blot
	7. Washing soda
	8. Blot
	9. Water
	10. Blot
Chewing gum	1. Freeze with ice cube
	2. Pulverise with blunt instrument
	3. Vacuum
	4. Solvent
	5. Wait several minutes
	6. Blot
	7. Repeat as necessary